STATISTICAL
METHODS
IN
ENGINEERING
EXPERIMENTS

CONSULTING EDITOR

RICHARD J. GROSH, *Purdue University*

STATISTICAL
METHODS
IN
ENGINEERING
EXPERIMENTS

Edwin M. Bartee

University of Alabama in Huntsville

CHARLES E. MERRILL BOOKS, INC., COLUMBUS, OHIO

Dedicated to
Professor George C. K. Johnson

Library of Congress Catalog Card Number: 66–18754

Preface

The primary objective of this book is to introduce to the engineer fundamental statistical methods within the framework of the experimental process. A further objective is to present the fundamental principles of scientific method and to relate it to the decision-making process that is so basic to engineering design. More specifically, the book has been written with the following considerations:

1. Statistical theory is presented from the viewpoint of the calculus.

2. The subject is presented from the "experimental viewpoint" of an engineer, rather than the "statistical viewpoint" of a statistician.

3. An attempt is made to balance theory with application, according to the needs of the engineer.

4. Examples and exercises have been drawn from authentic research data in the basic engineering sciences.

5. One of the most important features of the book's organization is the separation of theory and analysis from interpretation.

Topics related to interpretation, such as hypothesis testing, risk, and inference, are somewhat foreign to traditional engineering subject matter. Experience in teaching statistical methods has indicated that the engineer is generally more receptive to such topics after he has been introduced to statistical theory and analysis through more familiar mathematical methods.

The book is organized into three basic phases:

1. Theory (Chaps. 2 and 3)
2. Analysis (Chaps. 4 and 5)
3. Interpretation (Chaps. 6, 7, and 8)

Chapter 1 provides a discussion of the scientific method as it is related to engineering. The important topic of randomization in experiments is presented in Chapter 9.

A mathematical background through integral and differential calculus is required. Chapters 2 through 8, as a minimum, should be covered to obtain a complete study of the fundamental statistical process from theory to interpretation.

The early manuscripts of this book have been used as supplementary lectures in a course made up of engineering students from many disciplines, principally: electrical, industrial, mechanical, and engineering mechanics.

I am indebted to the Literary Executor of the late Sir Ronald A. Fisher, F.R.S., Cambridge, to Dr. Frank Yates, F.R.S., Rothamsted, and to Messrs. Oliver & Boyd Ltd., Edinburgh, for permission to reprint Tables III, IV, and XXXIII from their book *Statistical Tables for Biological, Agricultural and Medical Research.*

The successful completion of this book was possible because of the assistance, suggestions, and encouragement of many fine students, colleagues, and friends. I wish to thank particularly Mr. R. M. Wyskida, Mr. J. A. Svestka, Mr. L. S. Yarbrough, Mr. G. E. Webb, Mr. R. J. Fischer, Mr. W. W. Zbinden, Dr. Charley Scott, Mr. John M. Buterbaugh, Mrs. Patricia Campbell, Mrs. Ursula Vann, and Mrs. Earline Morgan.

Edwin M. Bartee

Huntsville, Alabama
March 1, 1966

Table of Contents

List of Figures   xi
List of Tables   xiii
Definition of Statistical Symbols   xv

Chapter 1
THE SCIENTIFIC METHOD IN ENGINEERING **1**

1.1   The Scientific Method 1
1.2   Basic Procedure in the Scientific Method 3
     Statement of the problem. Conducting a search.
     Preparation for experimentation.
1.3   Experimental Procedure 4
1.4   Summary 6

Chapter 2
THEORETICAL DATA DISTRIBUTIONS **8**

2.1   Introduction to Probability 9
     Sets. Sample spaces. Events. Simple probability.
     Some basic concepts of probability.
2.2   The Binomial Distribution 16
     Discrete frequency functions.
2.3   Binomial Moments and Parameters 20
     The second moment
2.4   The Poisson Distribution 24
2.5   The Normal Distribution 27
     Moments of the normal distribution
2.6   Other Data Distributions 33
2.7   Exercises 33

Chapter 3
THE THEORY OF SAMPLING............................ **36**

    3.1 Random Sampling............................ 37
    3.2 Empirical Methods........................... 38
    3.3 Unbiased Estimates.......................... 40
    3.4 Degrees of Freedom......................... 43
    3.5 Covariance................................. 43
    3.6 Other Measures of Central Tendency........... 45
          The median. The mode. The geometric mean.
          Harmonic mean. Quadratic mean.
    3.7 Other Measures of Variation.................. 47
          The range. The average deviation. The quartile
          deviation.
    3.8 The Distribution of a Sample Mean............ 48
    3.9 Exercises.................................. 52

Chapter 4
ANALYSIS OF EXPERIMENTS WITH ONE
INDEPENDENT VARIABLE............................ **55**

    4.1 Level of Variable not Predetermined............ 56
          Linear regression. Analysis of regression variance.
          Curvilinear regression.
    4.2 Levels of Variable Predetermined.............. 72
          Estimate of experimental variance. The regression
          method. The analysis of variance method.
    4.3 Exercises.................................. 81

Chapter 5
ANALYSIS OF EXPERIMENTS WITH MULTIPLE
INDEPENDENT VARIABLES........................... **83**

    5.1 Levels of Variables not Predetermined.......... 83
          Multiple linear regression. Analysis of multiple
          linear regression variance.
    5.2 Levels of Variables Predetermined.............. 92
          The analysis of variance method.
    5.3 Exercises.................................. 97

Chapter 6
THE THEORY OF INTERPRETATION............... **98**

6.1 Some Considerations in Formal Logic.......... 99
The nature of facts. The nature of proof. The nature of cause and effect. The nature of evidence. The nature of hypotheses.
6.2 Interpretation of Probability................... 102
Probiablity as a measure of belief. Probability as relative frequency. Probability as the truth-frequency of types of arguments.
6.3 Statistical Inference.......................... 104
6.4 The Neyman-Pearson Theory of Inference....... 105
Levels of significance. Power of a test.
6.5 Confidence Intervals as Inference.............. 107

Chapter 7
INTERPRETATION OF VARIANCES................ **108**

7.1 The Distribution of Mean Squares............. 108
7.2 The Distribution of a Random Variable
When σ is Unknown........................ 111
7.3 Interpretation of Experimental Variance When
Levels of Variable are not Predetermined....... 113
The coefficient of correlation. The distribution of r. Standard error of the regression estimate. Confidence limits for the regression estimate. Curvilinear and multiple correlation.
7.4 Interpretation of Experimental Variance When
the Levels of the Variables are Predetermined..... 121
Test for significance of mean squares. Components of variance. The distribution of variances. Confidence limits for variances.
7.5 Exercises.................................... 131

Chapter 8
INTERPRETATION OF MEANS..................... **132**

8.1 Interpretation of a Sample Mean When
σ is Known.................................. 133
Test of hypothesis related to μ. Confidence limits for μ.

8.2   Interpretation of μ When σ is Unknown.........   133
8.3   Difference Between Two Sample Means..........   140
      When $\sigma_{y_1}^2$ and $\sigma_{y_2}^2$ are known. When $\sigma_{y_1}^2$ and $\sigma_{y_2}^2$
      are unknown.
8.4   Difference Between Several Sample Means.......   144
      Comparisons made prior to experimentation.
      Comparisons made after experimentation.
8.5   Exercises...................................   147

Chapter 9
RANDOMIZATION IN EXPERIMENTS....................   **148**

9.1   The Nature of Bias...........................   149
9.2   Complete Randomization.......................   151
9.3   Single-Block Randomization...................   154
9.4   Dual-Block Randomization.....................   154
9.5   Multidual-Block Randomization................   157
9.6   Exercises...................................   159

APPENDICES...   **161**

A.   Combinatorial Analysis........................   161
B.   Special Frequency Functions...................   164
     Distribution functions. Joint continuous fre-
     quency functions.
C.   Interpretation of Frequency Data..............   167
D.   Data Sets for Exercises.......................   170
E.   Cumulative Probabilities of the Normal
     Probability Distribution......................   176
F.   Percentage Points of the χ^2 Distribution.........   177
G.   Critical Values for the F Distribution...........   178
H.   Percentage Points of the t Distribution..........   182
I.   Table of Random Numbers.....................   183
J.   Fortran Computer Programs for Basic
     Statistical Operations........................   184

BIBLIOGRAPHY...   **200**

INDEX...   **202**

List of Figures

2.1.	The Sample Space for Two Tosses of a Coin...............	10
2.2.	The Sample Space for Three Tosses of a Coin..............	11
2.3.	A General Sample Space................................	12
2.4.	A General Sample Space................................	13
2.5.	Graph of the Probabilities for $x =$ No. of Heads From the Toss of Two Coins................................	17
2.6.	Graph of the Probabilities of Getting Heads in the Toss of Three Coins....................................	18
2.7.	Comparison Between Histograms for Two and Three Coins..	19
2.8.	Moments of a Point Mass..............................	21
2.9.	A Histogram With an Infinite (or Large) Number of Rectangles...	27
2.10.	Moment of a Continuous Mass.........................	28
2.11.	A Continuous Distribution.............................	29
2.12.	The Standardized Normal Distribution...................	31
2.13.	A Normal Distribution Showing Standard Normal Values and Absolute Values on Abscissa......................	32
2.14.	Diagram of Example 2.6.3..............................	33
3.1.	The Mode of a Typical Histogram.......................	46
4.1.	An Estimated Linear Relationship.......................	58
4.2.	Linear Regression of Tensile Strength on Hardness........	62
4.3.	A Linear and Curvilinear Fit of Data....................	67
6.1.	The Relationship Between α and β Risk..................	105
6.2.	Typical Operating Characteristic Curve for an Assumed θ_0 and α......................................	106

7.1. A General Form of the χ^2 Distribution.................. 109

7.2. General Form of F Distribution......................... 111

7.3. The t Distribution...................................... 113

7.4. Distribution of r When $n = 9$.......................... 116

7.5. 90% Confidence Limits for the Regression of Tensile
Strength on Hardness of Copper Wire................... 119

8.1. The Operating Characteristic Curve for a One-Tail Test of
the Hypothesis, H_0: $\mu_0 = 6.0$, given $\sigma = 1.25$ and
$\alpha = 0.05$ in Example 8.2.2............................. 137

9.1. Illustration of Bias Effects............................. 150

9.2. Two Experimental Designs Superimposed................ 157

B.1. Graph of the Distribution Function $F(x)$ for the Toss
of Three Coins... 165

B.2. Graph of the Function $f(x, y) = e^{-(x+y)}$ 166

List of Tables

2.1. The Expected Outcomes from Two Tosses of a Coin........ 10
2.2. The Outcomes from Three Tosses of a Coin.............. 11
2.3. Probability of One Head for Toss of Two Coins........... 12
2.4. Probability of Getting at Least One Head with Two Coins... 13
2.5. Occurrence of Heads from the Toss of Three Coins........ 18
3.1. Continuous Random Variable x......................... 37
3.2. Sample Results for Example 3.2.1...................... 39
3.3. Data from Three Tosses of Coin in Table 2.2............. 50
4.1. General Sample Data for an Experiment................. 57
4.2. Data Pertaining to Example 4.1.2...................... 59
4.3. Test Results for Ten Specimens of Copper Wire........... 60
4.4. General Analysis of Regression Variance................. 64
4.5. General ANOVA Table for Regression Variance.......... 65
4.6. Analysis of Variance Table for Example 4.1.5............. 66
4.7. General Experimental Layout........................... 73
4.8. General ANOVA Table................................ 76
4.9. General ANOVA Table................................ 78
4.10. Data for Example 4.2.3................................ 78
4.11. ANOVA Table for Example 4.2.3....................... 79
4.12. Power Output in Watts for Four 50-KVA 2400/240 Volt
     Transformers... 80
5.1. Input-Output Data for Multidimensional Experiment....... 85
5.2. Experimental Data for Example 5.1.2................... 87
5.3. Calculations for Example 5.1.2......................... 90
5.4. General ANOVA for Multiple Regression Variance......... 91

5.5. General Experimental Data for Multiple
     Independent Variables................................. 93
5.6. General ANOVA Table for Experiment with Two
     Independent Variables................................. 94
5.7. Data for Example 5.2.2................................. 94
5.8. Calculations for Example 5.2.2.......................... 95
5.9. ANOVA Table for Example 5.2.2.......................... 96
7.1. Analysis of Linear Regression Variance................... 113
7.2. An ANOVA Table for Example 7.3.1..................... 114
7.3. General ANOVA Table with EMS....................... 125
7.4. General ANOVA Table with EMS....................... 126
7.5. ANOVA Table for Example 4.2.3 with EMS.............. 128
8.1. A General Experiment.................................. 132
8.2. Hardness Test Data for a Steel Alloy.................... 139
8.3. Yield of Chemically Pure Vanillin in Pounds of Vanillin
     (Times 10) per Gallon of Waste for Example 8.3.2......... 142
9.1. A 3 × 3 Matrix Experiment with b Units of Bias........... 149
9.2. Cell Responses for a Biased Experiment................... 150
9.3. ANOVA for Data in Table 9.2........................... 151
9.4. A 3 × 3 Matrix Experiment............................. 152
9.5. Top Two Rows of Random Numbers from Appendix I..... 152
9.6. A 3 × 3 Matrix Experiment............................. 152
9.7. A 3 × 3 Matrix Experiment............................. 152
9.8. A Completely Randomized Experimental Plan............. 153
9.9. ANOVA Table for Random Numbers in Table 9.8.......... 153
9.10. A Randomized-Block Experimental Plan.................. 154
9.11. A Double Randomized-Block Experiment Plan............. 155
9.12. A 3 × 3 Latin-Square Experimental Plan.................. 155
9.13. Tool Life, in Hours, for Various Speeds, Feeds, and
     Tool Steel Alloys..................................... 156
9.14. A Multidual-Block Experimental Plan.................... 158
9.15. Tool Life Data for Example 9.5.1....................... 158
C.1. Computation for Frequency Data........................ 168

Definition of Statistical Symbols

A.D.	Average deviation.
α	Error of the first kind or Type I error.
α'	The risk of a first kind when comparisons between mean levels of variables are made after experimentation.
ANOVA	Analysis of variance.
b_0	The best estimate of β_0.
b_p	The best estimate of β_p.
β	Error of the second kind or Type II error.
β_0	The true intercept in a regression equation.
β_p	The slope in a regression equation where p can designate the number of independent variables in a multiple regression or the order of the exponent in curvilinear regression.
C	Covariance sum of squares.
χ^2	A random variable related to the deviation of actual data from expected data.
χ_α^2	The critical value for the random variable χ^2 for a given α.
Cov.	Covariance.
δ	Deviation or difference.
e	The natural number $= 2.718284 +$
e_i	Estimated error in the ith response.
e_{ij}	Best estimate of ε_{ij}.
E	"Expected value" operator.
E_0	Particular event.
ε_i	The random or residual error in the ith response of a variable, with mean of zero and variance the same for all responses.
ε_{ij}	The random error in the ith level of one variable and the jth level of another variable.
f	Frequency function of, or function of.
$f\begin{pmatrix} m \\ n \end{pmatrix}$	The frequency function of m occurrences of an event from n trials.

$f(x, y)$	The joint frequency function of x and y.
$f(x)$	The frequency function of x.
$f(y)$	The frequency function of y.
F	A random variable related to sample variances.
$F(x)$	The distribution function of x.
F_α	The critical value for the random variable F for a given α.
g	The geometric mean.
H	Head on a coin.
H	The harmonic mean.
H_0	Null hypothesis.
H_1	Alternate hypothesis.
i	The ith trial or response.
j	The jth trial or response.
k	Total number of columns.
m	Total number of occurrences of an event.
M.S.	Mean square.
$M(\Theta)$	A moment generating function.
μ	The mean of a theoretical distribution.
μ'	Moment about the origin.
μ_k	The kth moment about the mean of a theoretical distribution.
μ_k'	The kth moment about the origin.
n	Total number of trials or responses in a sample.
N	Total number of responses in more than one sample with n responses in each sample.
n_j	Number of responses in the jth column.
$\binom{n}{r}$	A combination of n things taken r at a time.
ν	Degrees of freedom.
p	Probability an event will occur.
p	Total number of independent variables in a multiple regression or the order of the exponent in a curvilinear regression.
P	The probability of.
$_nP_r$	A permutation of n things taken r at a time.
q	Probability an event will not occur.
Q	Quadratic mean.
Q	Quartile deviation.
Q_1	First quartile.
Q_3	Third quartile.

r	An estimate of the true coefficient of correlation.
r^2	An estimate of the true coefficient of determination.
$R_{y.12...p}$	The coefficient of curvilinear or multiple correlation.
ρ	The true coefficient of correlation.
ρ^2	The true coefficient of determination.
s	The standard deviation of a sample.
s^2	The variance of a sample.
s_y	The standard deviation of a sample drawn from the y variable.
s_y^2	The variance of a sample drawn from the y variable.
$\hat{s}$	An estimate of σ.
$\hat{s}^2$	An unbiased estimate of σ^2.
$\hat{s}_y$	An estimate of σ_y.
$\hat{s}_y^2$	The unbiased estimate of σ_y^2.
S.S.	Sum of squares.
σ	The standard deviation of a theoretical distribution.
σ^2	The variance of a theoretical distribution.
$\sigma_{\bar{x}}$	The standard error of a mean.
$\sigma_{\bar{x}}^2$	The variance of a mean.
σ_y	The standard deviation of the y variable.
σ_y^2	The variance of the y variable.
σ_c^2	The component of variance attributable to the cth column variable.
σ_e^2	The component of variance attributable to experimental error.
σ_r^2	The component of variance attributable to the rth row variable.
Σ	The sum of.
t	A random variable related to small sample sizes.
t'	A random variable, larger than t, related to mean levels after experimentation.
t_α	The critical value of the random variable t for a given α.
t_j	The best estimate of τ_j.
T	Tail on a coin.
τ_i	The real effect of the ith level of a random variable.
τ_j	The real effect of the jth level of a single independent variable arranged in the columns of an experimental matrix.

τ_{cj} The real effect of the jth level of the cth independent variable arranged in the columns of an experimental matrix when crossed with r row variables.

θ A general parameter.

υ_{ri} The real effect of the ith level of the rth independent variable arranged in the rows of an experimental matrix when crossed with c column variables.

x A random variable, usually independent.

x_i The ith trial or response of the variable x.

$\bar{x}$ The arithmetic mean of a sample drawn from the variable x.

$\bar{x}_c$ Critical value of $\bar{x}$ where H_0 is rejected at α risk and H_1 is accepted at β risk.

y A random variable, usually dependent.

y_i The ith trial or response of the variable y.

y_i' The regression estimate of y_i.

$y_{.j}$ Total of n_j responses in the jth column.

$y_{..}$ Grand total of N responses in more than one sample with n responses in each sample.

y_{ijp} The response in the ith level of c column variables and the jth level of r row variables when $p = c + r$.

$y_{.jp}$ Total of n responses in the jth level of c column variables of an experimental matrix when crossed with r row variables where $p = c + r$.

$\bar{y}$ The arithmetic mean of a sample drawn from the variable y.

$\bar{y}_{.j}$ Mean of n_j responses in the jth column.

$\bar{y}_{..}$ Grand mean of N responses in more than one sample with n responses in each sample.

$y_{..p}$ Grand total of N responses in an experimental matrix with c column variables and r row variables where $p = c + r$.

$\bar{y}_{..p}$ Grand mean of N responses in an experimental matrix with c column variables and r row variables where $p = c + r$.

$\bar{y}_{.jp}$ Mean of n responses in the jth column of c column variables in an experimental matrix crossed with r row variables where $p = c + r$.

z A standard normal variable or random variable.

z' A special normal random variable.

z_α The critical value of the standard normal variable, z, for a given α.

CHAPTER 1

The Scientific Method in Engineering

Experimental methods have become increasingly important to engineers in recent years as the use of scientific information in engineering design has attained greater importance. In the recent past an engineering investigation was usually a mere informal test or trial run. Since the advent of the electronic computer, however, modern engineering has had a greater opportunity to use the *scientific method* in the engineering design process. The need for inquiry now requires that methods be more sophisticated and, generally, more valid than formerly.

Rarely is the modern engineer concerned with a design problem that does not involve several other engineers. When such is the case, it is important that certain valid methods be used so that a medium of "intelligence" is provided between the individuals. The significance and complexity of many modern engineering problems also require that the engineer communicate not only with other engineers but also with a variety of non-engineers. This list could include physicists, chemists, biologists, mathematicians, computer technicians, managers, accountants, and so forth. When contact with other *disciplines* is required, the communication problem is vastly increased, giving further emphasis to the need for more universal and objective methods of professional conduct.

Before we consider experimental methods in detail, we will consider some fundamental principles of the scientific method, of which experimentation is a major part.

1.1 The Scientific Method

Scientific method is the persistent *application of logic* as the common denominator of all reasoned knowledge. It is concerned with the way we test impressions and opinions by examining the best available evidence for and against them. Even though such methods have been traditionally related to the basic sciences, it would be most unscientific to attempt to restrict the use of such methods in other areas of inquiry where there is a need for testing impressions and opinions by applying sound logic to available information.

The scientific method is not the only method used for arriving at conclusions about unknown phenomena. Other such methods are:

1. *The method of tenacity.* This method is primarily based upon habit and inertia. The justification for a particular conclusion is primarily based upon traditional belief that has rejected all contradictory evidence.

2. *The method of authority.* With this method all questions of inquiry are answered by consultation with an authority who is presumed to have superior knowledge. A conclusion is reached when the belief of this authority is determined.

3. *The method of intuition.* This method could also be considered as an appeal to an "authority." With this method certain conclusions are made because they are considered to be "self-evident" or "obvious." In such cases, the *meaning* of the belief becomes the basis for its truth.

These three methods are in common use and as long as the human being is involved in his own inquiry, they will apparently continue to exist. Such methods often lack the clarity and accuracy that are required in engineering activities where it is necessary to establish a consensus of belief independent of our passions. The scientific method differs radically from these methods by encouraging and developing the utmost possible *doubt* so that any remaining *belief* is supported by the best available *evidence*. The scientific method is dedicated toward incorporating all new evidence, as it develops, so that a progressive cycle of belief and doubt may result.

The scientific method enables us to discover possible alternatives to propositions that we may regard as truisms, or as necessarily true. In this process, *formal logic* aids us to devise ways of formulating our propositions so that their possible alternatives become clear. Such concepts are discussed further in Chapter 6.

1.2 Basic Procedure in the Scientific Method

The fundamental process in the scientific method may be described as a repetition of *analysis* and *synthesis*. Even the most restricted portions of engineering activity are too complex to be comprehended in complete and exact detail by human effort. Under increasingly refined observation, it becomes impossible to neglect interactions with the rest of the universe. It is, therefore, necessary to ignore many of the actual features of a problem under study. We must thus abstract an idealized version of the real problem, with the expectation that it will be a useful approximation.

It is usually desirable to break the idealization into a number of parts for separate treatment, that is, to *analyze* the problem. Basically, such an analysis is concerned with the identification of parts that are independent of one another, or mutually interacting in simple ways. Not only are certain features of the problem abstracted to create idealized situations, but certain aspects of these idealized situations are often altered to produce simplified parts. Such a function is called *simplification*.

When these parts of the problem have been solved, the application of this knowledge to an observable situation usually requires that the parts be put together. In other words, an approximation to a real situation may be constructed by *synthesis* from relatively simple parts. This may be the only situation capable of experimental or observational test. This cycle of analysis and synthesis can be systematically and effectively followed by the use of certain specific procedures.

1.2.1 Statement of the Problem. It may seem trivial to give emphasis to what should be an obvious step in attacking a problem. However, there is probably no greater single source of waste and lost engineering effort than an imperfect *statement of the problem*. Many times the problem is a spurious one because it is based upon faulty information. Sometimes an effort toward definition will identify the problem as being trivial even though it is real. In other cases the problem is such that, even if it were solved, the solution would not be utilized.

1.2.2 Conducting a Search. Before beginning a new investigation, it is essential to find out the existing state of the field. The purpose of such a search should be primarily conducted (1) to determine whether the problem has already been investigated by others and (2) to acquire a broad general background in the field.

The general structure of material in a given field is as follows:

1. The most general sources are the various *encyclopedias*, which are useful for acquiring a first view of a field.

2. Beyond the general encyclopedias are the works designed for a particular area. In many of these areas *literature guides* have been prepared that list the basic reference works, review and abstract journals, and the principal journals for original contributions.

3. At the next level of information most fields offer *handbooks* that serve as summary material in the field.

4. The next level of specialization is formed by the *books* in the field. Textbooks provide the basic material; monographs give much more detail.

5. The *review*, *abstract*, and *indexing journals* in a field serve as a valuable source of information on basic current papers and specialized publications.

The reading of such literature needs to be done with a critical reflective attitude of mind if originality and freshness of outlook are not to be lost. Merely to accumulate information is not sufficient.

1.2.3 Preparation for Experimentation. After relevant literature has been critically reviewed, the investigator is better prepared for collecting field data and/or equivalent observational inquiry. From such data more specific questions can be formulated by exposing the problem to detailed definition and analysis.

It is at this point that intelligent guesses, *hypotheses*, are considered in relation to the problem. *Experiments* are then designed to investigate the most important hypotheses bearing on the most crucial questions.

1.3 Experimental Procedure

An experiment usually consists of making an event occur under known conditions, where as many extraneous influences as possible are eliminated and close observation is possible so that relationships between phenomena can be revealed. The "controlled experiment" is one of the most important concepts. In such a case there are two or more similar groups. One of the groups is called the "control" group and is held as the standard of comparison. The other groups are called "test" groups. These are subjected to a given set of defined conditions whose effect one wishes to determine. The groups are usually formed by *randomization*—a method of assigning individual specimens to each group, free of bias (see Chap. 9).

The traditional method of experimentation requires that the groups be as similar as possible in all respects except in the one variable factor under investigation. With the aid of modern statistical methods, however, it is now possible to plan experiments that test a number of variables at the same time.

As early as possible in an investigation, a simple crucial experiment should be carried out in order to determine whether or not the main hypothesis, under consideration, is true. A "breadboard" experiment, so to speak, can often save considerable time and lost effort in an investigation. The methods that are given in this book are quite conducive to such investigations.

Another general principle of a rather similar kind is the process of systematic elimination. One can often find the unknown more quickly by narrowing down the possibilities, systematically, rather than by making direct but blind guesses.

It is often good policy to start with a modest preliminary or "pilot" experiment. Apart from consideration of economy, it is seldom desirable to undertake at the outset an elaborate experiment designed to give a complete answer on all points. It is often better for the investigation to progress in stages from one point to the next, as the later experiments may require modification according to the results of earlier ones.

Occasionally quite a small experiment, or test, can be arranged so as to get a provisional indication of results when the evidence is too slender to justify a large experiment. Such sketchy experiments are justifiable only when their positive result would lead to a more elaborate verification of such results.

The essence of any satisfactory experiment is that it should be *reproducible*. If the results of the experiment continually fluctuate without a comparable change in the identified variables, it often means that some unrecognized factor is affecting the results, and the experiment is not reproducible.

Attention to experimental technique is very important in order to assure desirable results. This would, of course, include the equipment and measuring devices. These important considerations are not, however, a part of the scope of this book.

The careful recording of all details in experimental work is an elementary, but important, rule. The need to refer back to early information in the experiment can arise many times.

Whenever possible, the results of experiments should be assessed by some objective measurement. Such objective methods, called *statistical techniques*, are the main theme of this book. Such statistical methods are concerned not only with the analysis of the experiment after the data collection, but also with the design and planning phase of the experiment. The precision with which such methods can be used in the end is quite dependent upon the effectiveness of their consideration in experimental design.

When testing out a procedure for the first time, it is often impossible to estimate in advance how many specimens are required to ensure a decisive result. If cost of the specimens is of major concern, it may be necessary to conduct a sequence of small tests until the accumulated results are sufficient to satisfy statistical requirements. Special techniques are available for *random sampling* (Chap. 3) and for estimating the necessary size of the sample for it to be representative of the whole. The number required in the sample depends upon the variability of the responses and on the degree of error that will be tolerated in the results (Chap. 6).

Appropriate statistical techniques enable several variables to be included in one experiment (Chap. 5). This method has proved to be far superior, usually, to the method of considering each variable separately. More information is gained because each variable is examined in the light of a variety of circumstances. The traditional method of experimental isolation of a single variable often requires a somewhat arbitrary definition of that variable and testing under restricted, unduly simplified circumstances that can make the investigation invalid.

Statistics, like any other research technique, has its uses and its limitations. Its main value is in testing hypotheses (Chaps. 7 and 8), not in initiating discovery. In providing sufficient data for statistical analysis, the experimenter must not be tempted to do so at the expense of accurate observation.

The use of statistics does not reduce the importance of using common sense in interpreting results. Fallacy is especially likely to arise when dealing with field data in which there may be a significant difference between two groups. This does not necessarily mean that the difference is caused by the variable that is under consideration. It is possible that there is some other variable whose influence or importance has not been recognized. Such fallacies do not arise in well-designed experiments where the initial process of randomization assures a valid comparison of the groups [7] [15].*

1.4 Summary

This chapter has been devoted to a general discussion of the scientific method and experimental procedures. The chapters that follow are intended to provide certain theory, principles, and technique in the experimental process as it relates to the use of statistical methods. The material is presented in three principle phases:

---

* Bold numbers in brackets refer to items in Bibliography at the back of the book.

1. Theory
2. Analysis
3. Interpretation

Chapters 2 and 3 are devoted to introduction of the *theory* underlying probability, data distributions, and sampling. Chapters 4 and 5 are concerned with the *analysis* of experiments which are defined as:

1. Experiments with a single independent variable with the levels of the variable:
   (a) not predetermined
   (b) predetermined before experimentation
2. Experiments with multiple independent variables with the levels of the variables:
   (a) not predetermined
   (b) predetermined before experimentation

The theory and technique for *interpretation* of experimental results is presented in Chapters 6, 7, and 8. The important consideration of randomization in experiments is discussed in Chapter 9.

CHAPTER 2

Theoretical Data Distributions

The purpose of this chapter is to present certain fundamental concepts of statistical theory that are important to the understanding of experimental methods. As in any engineering problem, we must deal with both the *theoretical* and *empirical* aspects of experimental data. In this chapter we will consider the theoretical data distributions, and in Chapter 3 we will cover the theory of sampling as it is concerned with empirical methods.

The primary value of statistical method in engineering is to provide a *probabilistic* view of engineering design problems as opposed to a *deterministic* view. Obviously, no scientific phenomenon will be exactly true in a real-world situation. We can, for example, readily accept the basic law of physics

$$F = ma$$

that force equals mass times acceleration. However, at the same time that we accept this deterministic relationship, we do not expect to get the exact theoretical value for force when mass and acceleration are measured under ordinary conditions. If we should make several repetitive measurements of mass and acceleration, we would expect the calculated resultant force to be different to some degree, depending upon the sensitivity of the measuring instruments and the amount of variation inherent in the

8

particular case. Such a collection of repetitive measurements is called a "distribution of values." A real-world situation is said to be probabilistic when a distribution of results is expected. Therefore, the basis for understanding the nature of such *data distributions* is to understand some elementary principles of probability.

2.1 Introduction to Probability

The subject of probability can be approached from two viewpoints. One approach is from an axiomatic point of view, that is, as a phenomenon in pure mathematics. The engineer's interest in the subject is more in the applied realm. The theory of statistics is strongly based upon certain fundamental principles of probability as they relate to the outcomes of experiments. In this sense probability is thought of as the proportion of times that a certain event will occur if the experiment under observation is repeated indefinitely.

2.1.1 Sets. A set is a collection of well-defined elements. By convention, this may be expressed in the following manner:

$$S = \{x_1, x_2, \ldots, x_n,\}$$

where $x \in S$ means that x *belongs* to S, or x is *contained* in the set S. Similarly, $x \notin S$ means that x is *not* contained in S. A set that has no elements in it is called the *null* set, usually denoted by $\varnothing$.

If there are two sets, S and T, and it is desired to consider the whole of these two sets, then it may be said that the *whole* is a union of S and T; that is, the union of S and T are those elements belonging to S or T, or both. For example, if $S = \{x, y\}$ and $T = \{y, z\}$, then the union of S and T is denoted as $S \cup T$, where $S \cup T = \{x, y, z\}$.

Likewise, if it is desired to consider only those elements common to both S and T, this is called the intersection of S and T and is expressed as $S \cap T$, where in the above case, $S \cap T = \{y\}$.

2.1.2 Sample Spaces. The set of points representing the possible outcomes of an experiment is called the *sample space*, or the event space, of the experiment. For example, if an experiment should consist of tossing a coin twice and observing the results, we know *a priori* what the four outcomes will be. These are shown in Table 2.1.

If we designate a head by the point *one*, and a tail by the point *zero*, we can then plot the sample space for this experiment in the xy plane as in Fig. 2.1.

For three tosses of a coin we can tabulate the possible outcomes as shown in Table 2.2.

TABLE 2.1

The Expected Outcomes from Two Tosses of a Coin

First Toss	Second Toss
Head	Head
Tail	Head
Tail	Tail
Head	Tail

And the sample space for this experiment is shown in a three-dimensional space in Fig. 2.2.

The idea of the sample space serves as an introduction to the mathematical treatment of probability theory as it relates to the outcomes of experiments.

2.1.3   Events. An *event* is a special case of a set. In the previous simple experiment we may be concerned with a particular occurrence. We could be concerned with the occurrence of a head, of a tail, or of a head and tail. Such an occurrence is called an event.

An event is said to be *dependent* if its occurrence is influenced by the occurrence of another event. An *independent* event is, therefore, one whose occurrence is unaffected by the occurrence of another event. That is, any previous occurrence or nonoccurrence of an event has no effect upon the occurrence of a present or future event if the event is independent.

Two events are said to be *mutually exclusive* if the occurrence of one

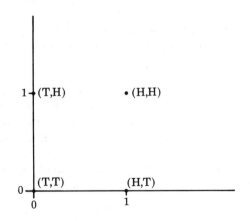

Fig. 2.1.   The Sample Space for Two Tosses of a Coin

TABLE 2.2

The Outcomes from Three Tosses of a Coin

	Toss	
1	2	3
H	H	H
H	H	T
H	T	T
T	T	T
T	T	H
T	H	H
T	H	T
H	T	H

event excludes the occurrence of another event. In Fig. 2.3, the events E_1 and E_2 are said to be mutually exclusive because they have no sample points in common.

2.1.4 Simple Probability. Each point in the sample space in Fig. 2.1 represents one possible outcome in a total of four outcomes. We can say that the probability of any one outcome occurring in two tosses of a *fair* coin is 1/4, the *sample space probability*. It is important to note that this would be true only if the coin is fair, that is, if the expected occurrence of heads and tails is equal on any toss.

For the tossing of two fair coins (the same as tossing one coin twice),

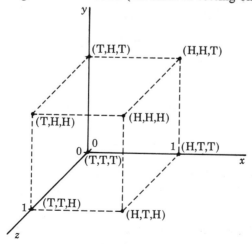

Fig. 2.2.   The Sample Space for Three Tosses of a Coin

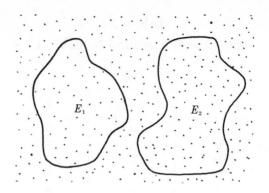

Fig. 2.3. A General Sample Space

we can calculate the probability of getting the event, the occurrence of a head, as in Table 2.3.

TABLE 2.3

Probability of One Head for Toss of Two Coins

Points in a Sample Space	Sample Space Probability	Occurrence of One Head	Probability of One Head
H,H	1/4	No	0
H,T	1/4	Yes	1/4
T,H	1/4	Yes	1/4
T,T	1/4	No	0
			2/4

It can be seen that the probability (2/4) of getting one head in the experiment is the ratio of the number of sample points that correspond to the occurrence of one head to the total number of sample points. If we designate $P\{E_0\}$ as the probability of an event E_0 occurring, m as the number of sample points giving rise to E_0, and n as the total number of sample points, then

$$P\{E_0\} = \frac{m}{n} \tag{2.1}$$

providing a generalized statement of probability. If $P\{E_0\} = 0$, the occurrence of the event is impossible. If $P\{E_0\} = 1$, the occurrence of the event is a certainty.

2.1.5 Some Basic Concepts of Probability. Suppose that in our simple experiment we are interested in the probability of *at least* one head occurring in two tosses. This event would occur if a head fell on the first toss and a tail on the second toss, a tail fell on the first toss and a head on the second toss, or a head fell on both tosses. The probability of at least one head occurring is calculated in Table 2.4. The probability of getting at least one

TABLE 2.4

Probability of Getting at Least One Head with Two Coins

Points in a Sample Space	Sample Space Probability	Occurrence of at Least One Head	Probability of at Least One Head
H,H	1/4	Yes	1/4
H,T	1/4	Yes	1/4
T,H	1/4	Yes	1/4
T,T	1/4	No	0
			3/4

head in two tosses of a coin is therefore 3/4. The general notation for such an event is $P\{E_1 \cup E_2\}$, the probability that at least one of the events E_1 and E_2 will occur. A formula for this probability will now be derived.

The sample space in Fig. 2.4 represents the sample points corresponding to the occurrence of events E_1 and E_2. The points common to these two regions determine a region that has been labeled $E_1 E_2$. It is therefore clear that the region $E_1 E_2$ is part of the region E_1 and also part of the region E_2.

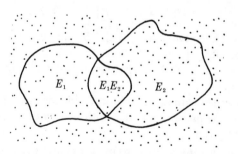

Fig. 2.4. A General Sample Space

It is also apparent that the number of sample points lying inside the two regions E_1 and E_2 is equal to the number of points inside E_1 plus the number lying inside region E_2, minus the number lying inside the common region $E_1 E_2$, because the points lying inside $E_1 E_2$ would be counted twice if no subtraction were made. As a probability statement we can then write

$$P\{E_1 \cup E_2\} = P\{E_1\} + P\{E_2\} - P\{E_1 \cap E_2\} \tag{2.2}$$

giving us the *addition theorem* of probability.

In our example, two tosses of a coin, we can calculate the probability from Eq. (2.1) of getting at least one head as follows:

$P\{E_1\}$ = Probability of a head on first toss, = 1/2

$P\{E_2\}$ = Probability of a head on second toss, = 1/2

$P\{E_1 \cap E_2\}$ = Probability of both heads, = (1/2)(1/2) = 1/4

Therefore:

$$P\{E_1 \cup E_2\} = P\{E_1\} + P\{E_2\} - P\{E_1 \cap E_2\}$$
$$= 1/2 + 1/2 - 1/4 = 3/4$$

If the events are *mutually exclusive*, that is, one event cannot occur if the other occurs, then Eq. (2.2) becomes

$$P\{E_1 \cup E_2\} = P\{E_1\} + P\{E_2\} \tag{2.3}$$

The probability of two events occurring together, $P\{E_1 \cap E_2\}$, is zero when such events are mutually exclusive. This particular probability is known as the *product theorem* of probability and can be written

$$P\{E_1 \cap E_2\} = P\{E_1\}P\{E_2\} \tag{2.4}$$

In our example, the probability of getting both a head in the first and second toss may be stated as:

$$P\{E_1 \cap E_2\} = P\{E_1\}P\{E_2\}$$
$$= (1/2)(1/2) = 1/4$$

where:

$$P\{E_1\} = 1/2, \quad P\{E_2\} = 1/2$$

2.1.6   Example. Given two alloys, A and B, with different fatigue life. The probability that alloy A will last 10 years is 0.8, and the probability that alloy B will last 10 years is 0.7. What is the probability that both A and B will last 10 years?

We are concerned with two events occurring together. This is, therefore, a case involving the product theorem with two independent events. From Eq. (2.4) we are given

$$P\{A \cap B\} = P\{A\}P\{B\} = (0.8)(0.7) = 0.56$$

2.1.7   Example. There are three white balls and two black balls in a box. If two balls are drawn in succession without the first one being replaced, what is the probability that both balls are black?

This is a case involving the product theorem with the events dependent. That is, the probability for the second ball is dependent upon the occurrence in the first draw because the balls are not replaced. Let E_1 be the event that a black ball is drawn on the first try, and let E_2 be the event that a black ball is drawn on the second try. We then know from Eq. (2.1) that

$$P\{E_1\} = \frac{m}{n} = \frac{2}{3+2} = 2/5$$

$$P\{E_2\} = \frac{m}{n} = \frac{1}{3+1} = 1/4 \quad \text{(since } E_1 \text{ has occurred)}$$

Therefore:

$$P\{E_1 \cap E_2\} = P\{E_1\}P\{E_2\}$$
$$= (2/5)(1/4) = 1/10$$

2.1.8   Example. What is the probability of drawing (a) either a king or a queen from a deck of playing cards on one draw, and (b) either a king or a spade from a deck of playing cards on one draw?

(a) This is a case involving the addition theorem with the two events being mutually exclusive. (Only one or the other can occur in one drawing.)

Let: K = drawing of a king.
              Q = drawing of a queen.

Then:

$$P\{K\} = \frac{m}{n} = \frac{4}{52} = 1/13$$

$$P\{Q\} = \frac{m}{n} = \frac{4}{52} = 1/13$$

and from Eq. (2.3) we have

$$P\{K \cup Q\} = P\{K\} + P\{Q\} - P\{K \cap Q\}$$
$$= (1/13) + (1/13) - 0 = 2/13$$

(b) This is a case involving the addition theorem because the events can occur together on one drawing of a card. (The king of spades.)

Let: K = drawing of a king.
              S = drawing of a spade.

Then:

$$P\{K\} = \frac{m}{n} = \frac{4}{52} = 1/13$$

$$P\{S\} = \frac{m}{n} = \frac{13}{52} = 1/4$$

Therefore:

$$P\{K \cup S\} = P\{K\} + P\{S\} - P\{K \cap S\}$$
$$1/13 + 1/4 - (1/13)(1/4) = 4/13$$

In this problem the first two terms fully account for the probability of a king and a spade occurring. The third term is therefore redundant and must be subtracted.

2.2 The Binomial Distribution

We will now observe the characteristics of experimental data and their distributions. A *distribution of data* is the characteristic domain within which the data occurs. A *theoretical distribution* is an expression of the expected distribution of certain data.

Suppose that we are concerned with the occurrence, or nonoccurrence, of an event in a particular experimental situation. If we let p be the probability that the event will occur and q be the probability that the event will not occur, we then know from the binomial expansion that

$$(q + p)^n = q^n + nq^{n-1}p + \frac{n(n-1)}{2} q^{n-2}p^2 + \ldots + p^n \qquad (2.5)$$

where n = number of trials, or repetitions, in the experiment.

Observing that Eq. (2.5) is a permutation* of n trials taken x at a time, we rewrite it

$$(q + p)^n = \sum_{x=0}^{n} \frac{n!}{x!(n-x)!} q^{n-x}p^x \qquad (2.6)$$

where x = number of successes.

We know from Eq. (2.3) that a set of mutually exclusive events will occur as the sum of their separate probabilities (the Addition Theorem). The right-hand side of Eq. (2.6) is therefore the sum of all the possible terms in the binomial expansion, giving the probabilities of the various possible results in their natural order.

The resulting probability is the probability of obtaining x successes in n independent trials of an event for which p is the probability of success in a single trial and is written

$$P(x) = \sum_{x=0}^{n} \frac{n!}{x!(n-x)!} q^{n-x}p^x \qquad (2.7)$$

2.2.1 Example. Two fair coins are tossed. What is the probability of getting one head?

The possible combinations of heads and tails for two coins are:

Coin 1	*Coin 2*
H	H
H	T
T	H
T	T

---

* Combinatorial analysis is reviewed in Appendix A, page 161.

From the above it follows that

Number of Heads	Probability of Occurrence
0	1/4
1	1/2
2	1/4

Therefore, the probability of getting one head is 1/2.
The distribution of the above probabilities is illustrated in Fig. 2.5.

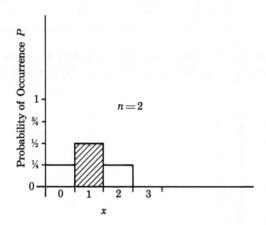

Fig. 2.5.   Graph of the Probabilities for x = Number of Heads from the Toss of Two Coins

The shaded portion, 50 per cent of the area included by the bar graph, represents the probability of getting one head from the toss of two coins.

2.2.2 Discrete Frequency Functions. The number of successes, x, in Eq. (2.7) can be considered as the number of sample points from a sample space corresponding to the tossing of a coin. In Example 2.2.1, x assumes the values of 0, 1, and 2. Such a numerically valued variable as this is called a *random variable*. Figure 2.5 illustrates the probability that the random variable x will assume any particular value in its domain. In other words, the probability that heads will not occur in the toss of two coins, or $x = 0$, is 1/4. Such a function $f(x)$ is called a *frequency function* of the random variable x. The random variable x, in this case, is said to be *discrete* since its values only occur as integers.

The frequency function for the case of the occurrence of heads with a toss of three coins can be determined *a priori*. From Table 2.2 it is known that in the toss of three coins, heads and tails can occur as summarized in Table 2.5.

TABLE 2.5

Occurrence of Heads from the Toss of Three Coins

Number of Heads	Number of Occurrences		Probability of Occurrence
0		1	1/8
1		3	3/8
2		3	3/8
3		1	1/8
	Total	8	

If we graph the above data, we produce the frequency function for the discrete random variable, the occurrence of heads, in Fig. 2.6.

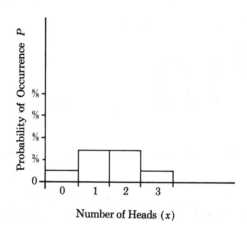

Fig. 2.6. Graph of the Probabilities of Getting Heads in the Toss of Three Coins

The areas of the bars represent the relative frequency, or probability, of getting 0, 1, 2, or 3 heads in the toss of three coins. Such a graph is called a *histogram*. The total area for the four bars in this graph is equal to one $(1/8 + 3/8 + 3/8 + 1/8 = 8/8 = 1)$.

If we superimpose the histogram for the expectancy of heads in the toss of two coins (Fig. 2.5) over that in Fig. 2.6, we get the result in Fig. 2.7. Notice that the amount of area (a) for the two-coin histogram that is excluded by the three-coin histogram is equal to the amount of area (b) that is added to the two-coin histogram by the three-coin histogram. The total area in each case is equal to one. Therefore, if x is considered to be a numerically valued variable within a particular set of possible results (a

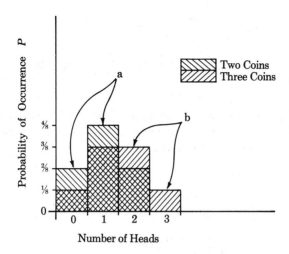

Fig. 2.7. Comparison Between Histograms for Two and Three Coins

random variable), we can write a single term of the binomial expansion in Eq. (2.7) as a frequency function

$$f(x) = \frac{n!}{x!(n - x)!}\, q^{n-x}p^x \tag{2.8}$$

Equation (2.8) is the general frequency function, or *binomial distribution*, from which the area (or probability) for any value of x can be determined. In the case of two coins, the probability of getting two heads is:

$$x = 2 \text{ heads}$$
$$n = 2 \text{ coins}$$
$$p = 0.5 \quad (\text{probability of head on one coin})$$
$$q = 0.5 \quad (\text{probability of tail on one coin})$$

$$f(x) = \frac{n!}{x!(n - x)!}\, q^{n-x}p^x$$

$$= \frac{2!}{2!(0)!}\, 0.5^0\, 0.5^2 = 0.25 \quad \text{or} \quad 2/8$$

In the case of three coins, the probability of getting two heads is:

$$x = 2 \text{ heads}$$
$$n = 3 \text{ coins}$$
$$p = 0.5$$
$$q = 0.5$$

$$f(x) = \frac{n!}{x!(n-x)!}\, q^{n-x}p^x$$

$$= \frac{3!}{2!(1)!}\, 0.5^1\, 0.5^2 = \frac{3\cdot 2\cdot 1}{2\cdot 1(1)}\, (0.5)(0.25)$$

$$= 0.375 \quad \text{or} \quad 3/8$$

Using Eq. (2.8), we can also calculate the probability of getting *at least* one head in the toss of two fair coins. Setting $x = 0$, we first calculate the probability of getting no heads. Thus:

$$n = 2, \quad x = 0, \quad p = 0.5, \quad q = 0.5$$

$$f(x) = \frac{n!}{x!(n-x)!}\, q^{n-x}p^x = \frac{2!}{0!(2)!}\, 0.5^2\, 0.5^0$$

$$= \frac{2}{(1)(2)}\, (0.25)(1) = 0.25$$

By knowing the probability of getting no heads, we can subtract this quantity from one and calculate the probability of *not* getting $x = 0$, or the probability of getting one or more heads. Thus:

$$P(x \geq 1) = 1 - P(x = 0)$$
$$= 1 - 0.25 = 0.75$$

Notice that the probability of getting two heads in the toss of three coins is $3/8 - 2/8 = 1/8$ more than in the toss of two coins. This difference is shown as an area (b) in Fig. 2.7.

2.3 Binomial Moments and Parameters

Frequency functions can be further understood and described by the use of theoretical moments for the discrete random variable. The kth moment about the origin of a theoretical distribution with a frequency function $f(x)$ is given by

$$\mu_k' = \sum_{x=0}^{\infty} x^k f(x) \tag{2.9}$$

Such moments are analogous to the concept of moments for a point mass in the study of mechanics. Consider the random variable x analogous to a distance d, from a line AB to a point mass m, with the frequency function $f(x)$ being analogous to this point mass (Fig. 2.8).

In this analogy,

$$\text{First moment} = d_1 m_1$$

For n number of points we have

First moment $= d_1m_1 + d_2m_2 + d_3m_3 + d_4m_4 + d_5m_5 + \ldots + d_nm_n$

$$= \sum_{i=1}^{n} d_i m_i \tag{2.10}$$

It follows that for a kth moment, Eq. (2.10) becomes

$$\sum_{i=1}^{n} d_i^k m_i$$

giving the kth moment of a point mass m about a line AB.

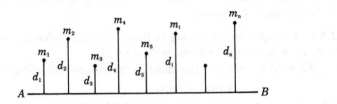

Fig. 2.8.   Moments of a Point Mass

Equation (2.9) can therefore be described as the kth moment about the origin of the distribution of x. The first moment of the distribution of x is found by applying Eq. (2.8) to Eq. (2.9) for $k = 1$ and getting

$$\mu_1' = \sum_{x=0}^{n} x \, \frac{n!}{x!(n-x)!} q^{n-x}p^x$$

By observation, when $x = 0$, $\mu_1' = 0$; thus

$$\mu_1' = \sum_{x=1}^{n} x \, \frac{n!}{x!(n-x)!} q^{n-x}p^x$$

Since $1! = 1$ and $0! = 1$, we can rewrite the above:

$$\mu_1' = \sum_{x=1}^{n} \frac{n!}{(x-1)!(n-x)!} q^{n-x}p^x \tag{2.11}$$

By factoring n and p, Eq. (2.11) becomes

$$\mu_1' = np \sum_{x=1}^{n} \frac{(n-1)!}{(x-1)!(n-x)!} q^{n-x}p^{x-1}$$

and setting $y = x - 1$, we get

$$\mu_1' = np \sum_{y=0}^{n-1} \frac{(n-1)!}{(n-1-y)!(y)!} q^{n-1-y}p^y$$

According to Eq. (2.7) the quantity being summed is the probability of y successes in $n - 1$ trials. Since the sum is over all possible values of y the sum must be equal to one;

hence, $$\mu_1' = np \qquad (2.12)$$

the first moment of the binomial distribution. This first moment about the origin is the theoretical mean average of the distribution. This is an important parameter of distributions that is noted by the symbol μ. We can therefore write Eq. (2.12) as

$$\mu = np \qquad (2.13)$$

which is the *mean* of the binomial distribution or the *most likely* number of occurrences of the event.

2.3.1   Example. In the tossing of three fair coins, what is the most likely number of heads that will occur on a toss?

We want to calculate the mean of the binomial distribution with

$n = 3$ trials (coins)
$p = 0.5 =$ probability of a head on one coin
$\mu = np = 3(0.5) = 1.5$ heads

On the average, 1.5 heads will occur.

2.3.2   Example. If a box contains twelve white balls and six black balls and if three balls are drawn, what is the most likely number of white balls that will be drawn?

Solution: Since we are concerned with the occurrence of white balls we must calculate the probability of a white ball occurring with $n = 3$ number of trials (balls). Thus with twelve white balls out of a total of eighteen balls we get

$$p = \frac{12}{12 + 6} = 2/3 = \text{probability of occurrence of a white ball}$$

$$\mu = np = (3)(2/3) = \text{two white balls}$$

2.3.3   The Second Moment. The second moment is calculated in a way similar to the first moment by using the identity $x^2 = x(x - 1) + x$. From Eqs. (2.8) and (2.9), we can write

$$\mu_2' = \sum_{x=0}^{n} x^2 \frac{n!}{x!(n - x)!} q^{n-x} p^x$$

$$= \sum_{x=0}^{n} [x(x - 1) + x] \frac{n!}{x!(n - x)!} q^{n-x} p^x$$

$$= \sum_{x=0}^{n} [x(x - 1)] \frac{n!}{x!(n - x)!} q^{n-x} p^x + \sum_{x=0}^{n} x \frac{n!}{x!(n - x)!} q^{n-x} p^x$$

and from Eq. (2.9) the second term is seen to be the first moment; thus,

$$\mu_2' = \sum_{x=0}^{n} x(x-1) \frac{n!}{x!(n-x)!} q^{n-x}p^x + \mu \qquad (2.14)$$

By observation, it can be seen that the summation term in Eq. (2.14) is equal to zero when $x = 0$ and $x = 1$. Thus, beginning with $x = 2$,

$$\mu_2' = \sum_{x=2}^{n} x(x-1) \frac{n!}{x!(n-x)!} q^{n-x}p^x + \mu$$

$$= \sum_{x=2}^{n} \frac{n!}{(x-2)!(n-x)!} q^{n-x}p^x + \mu$$

Factoring out $n(n-1)p^2$

$$\mu_2' = n(n-1)p^2 \sum_{x=2}^{n} \frac{(n-2)!}{(x-2)!(n-x)!} q^{n-x}p^{x-2} + \mu$$

and if $z = x - 2$,

$$\mu_2' = n(n-1)p^2 \sum_{z=0}^{n-2} \frac{(n-2)!}{(n-2-z)!(z)!} q^{n-2-z}p^z + \mu \qquad (2.15)$$

The summed portion of Eq. (2.15) is the probability of z successes in $n-2$ trials. Since the sum is over all possible values of z, its value is one. Therefore,

$$\mu_2' = n(n-1)p^2 + \mu$$

From Eq. (2.13), $\mu = np$; hence

$$\mu_2' = n(n-1)p^2 + np \qquad (2.16)$$

This is the second moment about the origin. This moment is more useful when it is calculated about the mean of a distribution. Thus, the kth moment about the *mean* of a theoretical distribution with frequency function $f(x)$ is given by

$$\mu_k = \sum_{x=0}^{\infty} (x - \mu_1')^k f(x)$$

From Eq. (2.13), $\mu = \mu_1'$; therefore

$$\mu_2 = \sum_{x=0}^{\infty} (x - \mu)^2 f(x)$$

$$= \sum_{x=0}^{\infty} x^2 f(x) - 2\mu \sum_{x=0}^{\infty} x f(x) + \mu^2 \sum_{x=0}^{\infty} f(x)$$

and from Eq. (2.9), this becomes

$$\mu_2 = \mu_2' - 2\mu\mu + \mu^2$$

Combining terms will give

$$\mu^2 = \mu_2' - \mu^2 \tag{2.17}$$

Using Eqs. (2.17) and (2.13) in Eq. (2.16), we obtain

$$\mu_2 = n(n-1)p^2 + np - n^2p^2$$
$$= -np^2 + np$$
$$\mu_2 = npq \tag{2.18}$$

Equation (2.18) is a common parameter of a distribution and is called the *variance* of the distribution. The notation, σ^2, is more commonly used for variance than μ_2. This variance and the mean, μ, represent the two parameters of a distribution. The mean measures the central tendency of the data or its most likely value. The variance measures the amount of spread or variation in the data in relation to the mean. The square root of the variance is called the *standard deviation* and is symbolized by σ. We can therefore write Eq. (2.18) as

$$\sigma = \sqrt{npq} \tag{2.19}$$

giving the standard deviation of the binomial distribution.

2.3.4   Example. In Example 2.3.2, what is the variance for the number of white balls that will be drawn if three balls are drawn from a box containing twelve white balls and six black balls?

Solution: From the previous calculations we know that

$$n = 3, \quad p = 2/3.$$

In this case, $q = 1 - 2/3 = 1/3$;

thus, $\sigma^2 = npq = (3)(2/3)(1/3) = (2/3)$

2.3.5   Example. A fair coin is tossed 100 times. What is the mean and standard deviation for the number of occurrences of heads?

Solution:

$$n = 100, \quad p = 0.5, \quad q = 0.5$$
$$\mu = np = 100(0.5) = 50$$
$$\sigma = \sqrt{npq} = \sqrt{100(0.5)(0.5)} = 5$$

2.4   The Poisson Distribution

When p in the binomial distribution approaches zero, the distribution approximates a form called the *Poisson distribution*. When n becomes large, the direct calculation of the binomial distribution becomes quite complex and the Poisson distribution can be conveniently used for approximating the binomial when p is small.

Named for its developer, the French mathematician Poisson, the distribution is defined by the exponential:

$$f(x) = \frac{e^{-\mu}\mu^x}{x!} \tag{2.20}$$

The parameter, μ, in Eq. (2.20) is the theoretical mean of the distribution expressed by the frequency function. This Poisson distribution is shown to be a good approximation to the binomial distribution by rewriting Eq. (2.8) thus

$$f(x) = \frac{n(n-1)\ldots(n-x+1)}{x!}(1-p)^{n-x}p^x$$

Multiplying both the numerator and denominator by n^x, we get

$$f(x) = \frac{n(n-1)\ldots(n-x+1)}{n^x x!}(1-p)^{n-x}(np)^x$$

We know from Eq. (2.13) that $\mu = np$; thus

$$f(x) = \frac{n(n-1)\ldots(n-x+1)}{n\cdot n\cdots n}(1-p)^{n-x}\frac{\mu^x}{x!}$$

and dividing through by n, the above becomes

$$f(x) = (1-1/n)(1-2/n)\ldots\left(1-\frac{x-1}{n}\right)(1-p)^{n-x}\frac{\mu^x}{x!}$$

$$= \frac{(1-1/n)(1-2/n)\ldots\left(1-\frac{x-1}{n}\right)}{(1-p)^x}(1-p)^n\frac{\mu^x}{x!} \tag{2.21}$$

Now, express $(1-p)^n$ as

$$(1-p)^n = [(1-p)^{-1/p}]^{-np} = [(1-p)^{-1/p}]^{-\mu}$$

and from the definition of e,

$$\underset{z\to 0}{\text{limit}}\,(1+z)^{1/z} = e$$

Letting $z = -p$, we get

$$\underset{p\to 0}{\text{limit}}\,[(1-p)^{-1/p}]^{-\mu} = e^{-\mu} \tag{2.22}$$

and also

$$\underset{n\to\infty}{\text{limit}}\,\frac{(1-1/n)(1-2/n)\ldots\left(1-\frac{x-1}{n}\right)}{(1-p)^x} = 1 \tag{2.23}$$

because $p \to 0$ as $n \to \infty$ when $np = \mu$ is fixed. Applying Eqs. (2.22) and (2.23) to Eq. (2.21), we get

$$\underset{n\to\infty}{\text{limit}}\,f(x) = \frac{e^{-\mu}\mu^x}{x!} \tag{2.24}$$

which is the same as Eq. (2.20). It can be seen from Eq. (2.24) that if the probability of success in a single trial p approaches zero while the number of trials n becomes infinite in such a manner that the mean $\mu = np$ remains fixed, then the binomial distribution will approach the Poisson distribution with mean μ.

2.4.1 Example. An average of one black ball is drawn when a group of ten balls are drawn from a large box containing many black and white balls. Find the probability that two black balls will be drawn in a group of ten balls by using

(a) the binomial distribution,

(b) the Poisson distribution.

Solution:

(a) From the binomial distribution, Eq. (2.8), we can calculate the probability of a given occurrence:

$$f\binom{2}{10} = \frac{n!}{x!(n-x)!}\, q^{n-x}p^x$$

where:
$$n = 10 \text{ balls}$$
$$x = 2 \text{ balls}$$
$$p = 1/10 = 0.1$$
$$q = 1 - p = 0.9$$

Thus: P (2 black from 10) $= \dfrac{n!}{x!(n-x)!}\, q^{n-x}p^x$

$$= \frac{(10)!}{(2)!(8)!}\,(0.9)^8(0.1)^2 = 0.19$$

(b) From Eq. (2.20), the Poisson distribution, we have for this case

$$f\binom{2}{10} = \frac{e^{-\mu}\mu^x}{x!}$$

where:
$$x = 2$$
$$\mu = np = 10(0.1) = 1.0$$

Thus: P (2 balls from 10) $= \dfrac{e^{-1.0}(1)^2}{2!} = \dfrac{1}{2e} = 0.18$

Observe that the two solutions are approximately the same.

2.4.2 Example. If the probability of drawing a black ball from a large box of balls is 0.001, what is the probability that out of 2,000 balls drawn exactly three black balls will be drawn?

Solution: We first calculate the mean μ. From Eq. (2.13) then,

$$\mu = np = (2{,}000)(0.001) = 2$$

If we use the binomial distribution, we get

$$f\binom{3}{2,000} = \frac{n!}{x!(n-x)!}\, q^{n-x}p^x$$

$$= \frac{2,000!}{3!(1,997)!}\,(0.999)^{1997}(0.001)^3$$

which is a very cumbersome problem to solve. If we use the Poisson distribution, we get

$$P(3) = \frac{e^{-\mu}\mu^x}{x!} = \frac{e^{-2}(2)^3}{3!} = 0.18$$

This example demonstrates the usefulness of the relationship between the Poisson and binomial distribution. Often, when the size of n is large, say >30, the Poisson distribution provides an easier method of solution, which is accurate when p is small.

2.5   The Normal Distribution

The two preceding distributions, the binomial and Poisson, are generally referred to as *discrete distributions* since they relate to the distribution of a discrete variable. Such variables assume only non-negative integral values.

It can be seen in Fig. 2.7 that as the number of coins is increased, the number of rectangles in the histogram will increase. The amount of area removed is equal to the area added since the total area will always equal one. If we should use an infinite number of coins, we would logically expect an infinite number of rectangles in the histogram, which would produce a smooth curve as seen by Fig. 2.9.

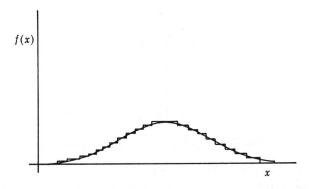

Fig. 2.9. A Histogram with an Infinite (or Large) Number of Rectangles

A frequency function $f(x)$ with an infinite number of possible values of x is called a *continuous frequency function* $f(x)$, and x is known as a *continuous random variable*. We may define a continuous frequency function as a function $f(x)$ whose first two moments exist and that meets the following criteria:

$$f(x) \geq 0 \tag{2.25}$$

$$\int_{-\infty}^{\infty} f(x)\, dx = 1 \tag{2.26}$$

$$\int_{a}^{b} f(x)\, dx = P\{a < x < b\} \tag{2.27}$$

where a and b are two values of x when $a < b$.

We will now consider the most useful of all distributions and the one with which the methods in this text are primarily concerned, the *normal or Gaussian distribution*. This distribution is known as a continuous random variable and is defined as follows:

$$f(x) = ce^{-1/2\left(\frac{x-a}{b}\right)^2} \tag{2.28}$$

where a, b, and c are parameters that make a frequency function. Outside the finite interval (a, b) the continuous frequency function is zero. The parameter c must be such that the total area of the distribution is equal to one.

2.5.1 Moments of the Normal Distribution. In Sec. 2.3 binomial moments were described as being analogous to the moments about a point mass m in the study of mechanics. A similar analogy can be made in the case of moments for the continuous-type normal distribution.

In Fig. 2.10 we have a continuous mass distribution dm at a distance D from a line AB, the sum of which can be written as the integral

$$\text{first moment} = \int D\, dm \tag{2.29}$$

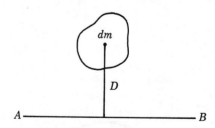

Fig. 2.10. Moment of a Continuous Mass

In mechanics, this first moment is called the *statical moment* of a mass. Corresponding to Eq. (2.29) for the first moment, the second moment is defined as

$$I = \int D^2 \, dm$$

and is called the *moment of inertia*. This second moment is an important concept in the theory of rotating bodies in mechanics [1].

The *statistical moments* for a continuous distribution are quite similar. Figure 2.11 illustrates a distribution lying between the finite interval (a, b). Let this interval be divided into n equal subintervals and let x_i be the midpoint of the ith subinterval. The sum of such intervals is written as

$$\sum_{i=1}^{n} x_i^k f(x) \, \Delta x \qquad (2.30)$$

where Δx is the width of a subinterval. The area of the shaded rectangle is the quantity $f(x_i) \, \Delta x$. The kth moment of this rectangular area about the origin is therefore $x_i^k f(x_i) \, \Delta x$. Expression (2.30) is therefore the sum of these moments. The kth moment of the $f(x)$ can be defined as the limit of this sum when the width of the subinterval approaches zero, since the rectangles approximate the area under the curve.

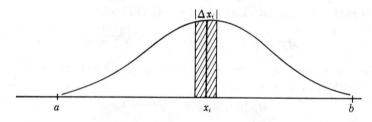

Fig. 2.11. A Continuous Distribution

The kth moment about the origin of a continuous distribution with frequency function $f(x)$ is therefore

$$\mu_k' = \int_{-\infty}^{\infty} x^k f(x) \, dx \qquad (2.31)$$

Let $g(x)$ be a function of x other than x itself. If $g(x) = x - \mu$, then the kth moment of $g(x)$ would be the kth moment of x about its mean. A general definition using the term $g(x)$ would shift the moments about the origin to moments about the mean. We can therefore say that if $f(x)$ is the frequency function of the random variable x, the kth moment of the function $g(x)$ is given by

$$\mu_{k,g(x)}' = \int_{-\infty}^{\infty} g^k(x) f(x) \, dx \qquad (2.32)$$

Theoretical moments can be directly calculated from both Eqs. (2.31) and (2.32). However, a different method involving the *moment generating function* will be used so that the characteristics of the normal distribution may be illustrated.

The moment generation function of a random variable x with frequency function $f(x)$ is given by

$$M_x(\Theta) = \sum_{x=0}^{\infty} e^{\Theta x} f(x) \qquad (2.33)$$

being a function of the parameter Θ, a mathematical device that is introduced to assist in the determination of moments.

From Eq. (2.33) then, we can observe that the moment generating function for a continuous variable is

$$M_x(\Theta) = \int_{-\infty}^{\infty} e^{\Theta x} f(x) \, dx \qquad (2.34)$$

As before, we will generalize the definition of the moment generating function by substituting $e^{\Theta g(x)}$ for the term, $e^{\Theta x}$ in Eq. (2.34). The moment generating function of $g(x)$ is given by

$$M_{g(x)}(\Theta) = \int_{-\infty}^{\infty} e^{\Theta g(x)} f(x) \, dx \qquad (2.35)$$

If $g(x) = x - \mu$, then Eqs. (2.35) and (2.28) become

$$M_{x-\mu}(\Theta) = c \int_{-\infty}^{\infty} e^{\Theta(x-\mu)} \cdot e^{-1/2\left(\frac{x-\mu}{b}\right)^2} dx$$

giving an expression of the moment about the mean. If we let $z = (x - \mu)/b$, then $dx = b \, dz$ and

$$M_{x-\mu}(\Theta) = bc \int_{-\infty}^{\infty} e^{\Theta b z - z^2/2} \, dz$$

If we complete the square in the exponent as follows:

$$\Theta b z = \frac{z^2}{2} = -\frac{1}{2}(z - \Theta b)^2 + \frac{1}{2}\Theta^2 b^2$$

then,

$$M_{x-\mu}(\Theta) = bc e^{(1/2)\Theta^2 b^2} \int_{-\infty}^{\infty} e^{(-1/2)(z-\Theta b)^2} \, dz$$

If $t = z - \Theta b$, then $dz = dt$ and

$$M_{x-\mu}(\Theta) = bc e^{(1/2)\Theta^2 b^2} \int_{-\infty}^{\infty} e^{-t^2/2} \, dt$$

and from any standard table of integrals, we get

$$M_{x-\mu}(\Theta) = \sqrt{2\pi} \, bc e^{(1/2)\Theta^2 b^2} \qquad (2.36)$$

The moment generating function for $\Theta = 0$ is always equal to one. Therefore, in Eq. (2.36) the term $\sqrt{2\pi} \, bc = 1$ and

$$M_{x-\mu}(\Theta) = e^{(1/2)\Theta^2 b^2} \qquad (2.37)$$

and by expanding the exponential we get

$$M_{x-\mu}(\Theta) = 1 + b^2 \frac{\Theta^2}{2} + b^4 \frac{\Theta^4}{8} + \cdots$$

It can be observed that only the even terms of the series are included and the odd powers are missing. This confirms a characteristic of any odd moment of x about its mean, μ. For any symmetrical distribution, such moments are always equal to zero.

The second moment of x about its mean is the coefficient of $\Theta^2/2!$; therefore, $b^2 = \mu_2 = \sigma^2$, or $b = \sigma$. Since $\sqrt{2\pi}\, bc = 1$, then $c = 1/\sigma\sqrt{2\pi}$; and since Eq. (2.28) is symmetrical, $a = \mu$. Therefore Eq. (2.28) becomes

$$f(x) = \frac{1}{\sigma\sqrt{2\pi}} e^{-1/2\left(\frac{x-\mu}{\sigma}\right)^2} \tag{2.38}$$

From Eq. (2.38) we can observe that the normal distribution can be completely described by its mean μ and its standard deviation σ.

We can now write

$$z = \frac{x - \mu}{\sigma} \tag{2.39}$$

which gives an expression for μ and σ in standardized form. Also, z is known as a *standardized normal random variable*. By combining Eqs. (2.39) and (2.38), we get

$$f(x) = \frac{1}{\sqrt{2\pi}} e^{-z^2/2} \tag{2.40}$$

which gives the standard form of the normal distribution with mean zero and σ of one. From Eq. (2.40) the integral becomes

$$P\left(z > \frac{x-\mu}{\sigma}\right) = \int_{\frac{x-\mu}{\sigma}}^{\infty} \frac{1}{\sqrt{2\pi}} e^{-z^2/2}\, dz = \alpha \tag{2.41}$$

where α is a term used for this probability (or area under the curve) in later applications. Equation (2.41) is illustrated graphically in Fig. 2.12.

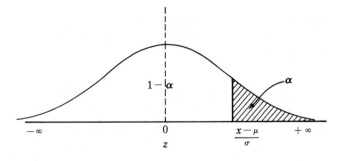

Fig. 2.12. The Standardized Normal Distribution

Appendix E, page 176, provides a tabulation of areas under the normal curve for different values of z. The area shown in the table is the quantity $1 - \alpha$, illustrated in Fig. 2.12.

2.5.2   Example. Suppose that we know μ and σ of a normal distribution to be 100 and 20 respectively. What is the probability of getting a value of 160 or less from the distribution?

Solution: Given: $\mu = 100$, $\sigma = 20$, $x = 160$.
We first calculate the value for z thus:

$$z = \frac{x_1 - \mu}{\sigma} = \frac{160 - 100}{20} = 3.00$$

This value is shown in Fig. 2.13 corresponding to $x_1 = 160$ on the abscissa.

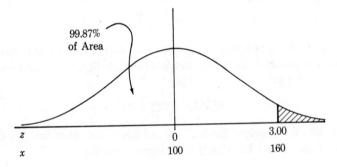

Fig. 2.13. A Normal Distribution Showing Standard Normal Values and Absolute Values on Abscissa

From Appendix E, the area for $z = 3.00$ is 0.9987. Thus, the probability of getting 160 or less is 0.9987, as illustrated in Fig. 2.13.

2.5.3   Example. If it is known that a normal distribution has a $\mu = 150$ and a $\sigma = 10$, for what value of δ will the quantity $\mu \pm \delta$ exclude 10 per cent of the possible values of x?

Solution:
For the symmetrical area to exclude 10 per cent of total area, 5 per cent must be excluded on each end (Fig. 2.14). To determine this area we refer to Appendix E and determine the value of z corresponding to the area that excludes 5 per cent on the upper end of the distribution. The area is 0.9500 and its corresponding z value is 1.645.

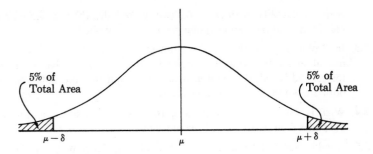

Fig. 2.14. Diagram of Example 2.6.3

If:
$$z = \frac{x - \mu}{\sigma} = \frac{\delta}{\sigma}$$

$$\therefore \delta = z\sigma$$
$$\delta = 1.645(10) = 16.45$$

Note: Since the distribution is symmetrical, $\delta = -16.45$ excludes 5 per cent of area on lower end.

2.6 Other Data Distributions

The three distributions presented in this chapter are particularly useful for the understanding of the subject matter in this book. Generally speaking, a theoretical data distribution can be derived for any phenomenon from which data is produced. Some of the more important distributions are listed below and described by their frequency function:

1. Geometric Distribution $\quad f(x) = q^{x-1}p$
2. Exponential Distribution $\quad f(x) = \Theta e^{\Theta x}$
3. Erlang Distribution $\qquad f(x) = \dfrac{\Theta e^{-\Theta x}(\Theta x)^{n-1}}{(n - 1)!}$

Where: Θ is a constant.

Certain distributions are related to the normal distribution. Several of these, the t distribution, the χ^2 distribution, and the F distribution will be dealt with later in Chapters 7 and 8.

2.7 Exercises (*Note:* Refer to Appendix D, page 170, for data sets.)

2.1. A die has three of its faces painted red and three painted white. If the die is rolled three times, describe the three-dimensional sample space.

2.2. Two balls are drawn in succession from a bowl containing five red, ten white, and fifteen green balls. If each ball is replaced after drawing, what is the probability of drawing (a) two white balls, (b) one white and one red, (c) no red ball, and (d) one green and no white?

2.3. In Problem 2.2, if the balls are not replaced when drawn, what is the probability in the drawing of two balls that (a) the first ball is green and the second is red, (b) the first is not green and the second is not red, (c) both are white, and (d) neither is red.

2.4. What is the probability of drawing (a) a jack, (b) a spade, and (c) a jack of spades from a deck of 52 playing cards?

2.5. A golfer has a dozen golf balls in his golf bag. Three balls are cheap, and the others are of premium quality. The golfer cannot distinguish between any of the balls. What is the probability of drawing a premium quality ball on the second draw assuming the golfer has lost his first ball?

2.6. Considering again the golfer in Problem 2.5 with the twelve balls: (a) What is the probability of drawing a premium quality ball on the third draw assuming the golfer has lost his first two balls? (b) What is the probability of having drawn three successive premium quality balls?

2.7. The golfer in Problem 2.5 is preparing to tee off on the first hole with a friend. He draws two balls for the first hole, one for himself, and one for his friend. (a) How many combinations of two golf balls may be drawn from his bag? (b) What is the probability of drawing two golf balls of premium quality? (c) What is the probability of drawing two cheap golf balls?

2.8. Given the discrete frequency function $f(x) = e^{-2}/x!$, when $x = 0, 1, 2, \ldots$, calculate (a) $P\{x = 1\}$; (b) $P\{x < 3\}$; (c) $P\{0 < x < 4\}$.

2.9. Calculate and graph the frequency function for the occurrence of boys and girls in a family of four children, assuming the equal probability for boys and girls.

2.10. Draw a histogram for the expectancy of the sum of spots on a pair of dice.

2.11. Evaluate (a) $\dfrac{5!}{2!4!}$, (b) $\dfrac{(8 - 2)!}{(25 - 19)!}$, (c) $\dfrac{1!2!}{0!4!}$.

2.12. Write the binomial expansion for (a) $(q + p)^4$, (b) $(q + p)^7$.

2.13. What is the probability of getting a total of 7 (a) twice, (b) at least twice in four tosses of two fair dice?

2.14. The actuarial tables for an insurance company give the probability of a particular aged male being alive in twenty years as 4/5. For four men who fall in this group, what is the probability that, in twenty years, (a) all four men will be alive, (b) three will be dead, (c) at least two will be alive?

2.15. Knowing that the number of accidents in a given period is Poisson distributed, what is the probability of having (a) 0, (b) 1, (c) less than 2 accidents if the average accident rate is 3?

2.16. The number of phone calls received during a period of time is Poisson distributed. If $\mu = 4$, what is the probability of getting (a) no calls (b) less than three calls (c) exactly two calls?

2.17. Given the continuous frequency function $f(x) = ce^{-x} \Big]_0^\infty$, determine the value of c.

2.18. Having the value of c in Problem 2.17, determine the mean and variance.

2.19. If x is normally distributed with $\mu = 2.00$, and $\sigma = 0.65$, find the probability that (a) $x > 2.00$, (b) $x < 1.35$, (c) $x > 3.30$.

2.20. Find the area under the normal curve for (a) $z \geq -1.30$, (b) $z \leq 2.30$, (c) $1.23 \leq z \leq 1.87$, (d) $-1.20 \leq z \leq 1.20$.

2.21. If z is normally distributed with mean zero and variance one, find (a) $P\{z \geq 1.96\}$, (b) $P\{-1.64 \leq z \leq 1.64\}$, (c) $1 - P\{-3.00 \leq z \leq 3.00\}$.

2.22. In the experiment related to data set 1, 35 participants noticed that the tubes were color coded while 44 participants did not. Compute (a) the first moment about the origin, and (b) the second moment about the mean of the theoretical distribution.

2.23. What is the theoretical distribution mentioned in Problem 2.22? Why is the Poisson distribution not a suitable approximation in this case?

2.24. Assuming data set 1b is normally distributed, what is the probability of getting a value of 1.30 or more from the distribution?

2.25. With respect to the participants in Problem 2.22, what is the probability that 25 or fewer participants would notice that the tubes were color coded?

CHAPTER 3

The Theory of Sampling

The purpose of Chapter 2 was to develop an understanding of the theory underlying data distributions in general and the normal distribution in particular. The normal distribution is a theoretical concept and in real-world situations, it cannot be measured exactly. When such is the case, we use *empirical* methods for estimating the parameters in question. Generally speaking, the primary concern of statistical method is related to the process of sampling an unknown phenomenon for the purpose of drawing conclusions, *a posteriori*, by observing the characteristics of the particular sample.

A *sample* can be viewed as an analog to a measuring instrument. For example, if we wish to measure the length of a small steel shaft, we could use an ordinary scale with 1/8 inch divisions or a micrometer that measures to the nearest 0.001 inch. In each case the result can provide a satisfactory measurement in a given situation. Obviously, the micrometer will measure the length of the shaft with more precision than the scale. Neither will measure the *exact* length. Theoretically, the exact length is impossible to measure because of the limited precision of any measuring instrument. Practically speaking, though, any degree of precision could be satisfactory in a particular situation.

A sample of n number of responses taken from an unknown distribution is quite similar. The *exact* distribution cannot be determined. A "measurement" of the distribution can be made by drawing a sample from it. This is called an *empirical* measurement. The precision of the sample is a function of its size n. Depending upon the requirements of a particular experiment, a sample of any size could give the necessary precision of measurement. As n increases, the precision at which the sample measures the true distribution increases.

3.1 Random Sampling

A sample is said to be *random* when n successive trials of the experiment are independent and the frequency function of the random variable remains constant from trial to trial. That is, if we let $f(x)$ be the frequency function of the continuous variable x and let a sample of size n be drawn, the resulting sample trials or *responses* will be noted by $x_{11}\, x_{12}, \ldots x_{1n}$. If a second sample of size n were drawn, the resulting responses would be denoted by $x_{21}, x_{22}, \ldots x_{2n}$, and similarly for k samples. The samples can be arranged as shown in Table 3.1.

TABLE 3.1
Continuous Random Variable x

First Sample	Second Sample	kth Sample
x_{11}	x_{21}	x_{k1}
x_{12}	x_{22}	x_{k2}
x_{13}	x_{23}	x_{k3}
.	.	.
.	.	.
.	.	.
x_{1n}	x_{2n}	x_{kn}

The two requirements for a random sample are, therefore:

(1) All x_{kn} responses are independent, i.e., the probability of one response occurring is unaffected by the occurrence of another response.

(2) The frequency function of the random variable x shall remain constant from response to response, or

$$f(x) = f(x_{kn})$$

3.1.1 Example. A fair coin is tossed five times, getting five consecutive heads. What is the probability of getting a head on the sixth toss?

Solution: This is a random sample of $n = 6$. The probability of a head is known to be 0.50. In such a random sample the frequency function for all tosses is the same.

If the successive tosses are independent, then the sixth toss is unaffected by the five previous tosses. Therefore,

$$P \text{ (a head on sixth toss)} = 0.5$$

3.2 Empirical Moments

In Sec. 2.6.1 we observed that the normal distribution can be described by μ, the first moment about the origin, and σ^2, the second moment about the mean. Empirically, the kth moment about the *origin* for a random sample of size n drawn from a frequency function of a continuous variable x is given by

$$m'_k = \frac{1}{n} \sum_{i=1}^{n} x_i^k \qquad (3.1)$$

As in the theoretical case, the first moment ($k = 1$) about the origin is the *sample mean*, $\bar{x}$, and is given by

$$\bar{x} = \frac{1}{n} \sum_{i=1}^{n} x_i \qquad (3.2)$$

which can be recognized as the common arithmetic average of a set of values.

A similar observation can be made in relation to the variance of a sample. The kth moment about the *mean* of a random sample of size n drawn from the frequency function of a continuous random variable x is given by

$$m_k = \frac{1}{n} \sum_{i=1}^{n} (x_i - \bar{x})^k \qquad (3.3)$$

As in the case of the theoretical distribution, the second moment about the mean of a sample is the *variance* s^2 of the sample; thus

$$s^2 = \frac{1}{n} \sum_{i=1}^{n} (x_i - \bar{x})^2 \qquad (3.4)$$

A random sample can therefore be fully described by three parameters: the mean $\bar{x}$, the variance s^2, and its size n. As in the case of the theoretical distribution, the sample *standard deviation* is the square root of the sample variance, denoted by s. These two parameters, s^2 and s, describe the characteristic of variation in responses of a sample. An important modification of these parameters, considered in Section 3.3, is concerned with more than the mere description of the sample.

3.2.1 Example. Ten random responses were drawn from a normal distribution with $\mu = 0$ and $\sigma = 10$. The results are shown in Table 3.2.

TABLE 3.2

Sample Results for Example 3.2.1

Trial Number	x	x^2
1	$+4$	16
2	-18	324
3	$+16$	256
4	-4	16
5	$+8$	64
6	$+2$	4
7	-4	16
8	$+6$	36
9	-10	100
10	$+10$	100
	$\sum x = +10$	$\sum x^2 = 932$

Calculate the sample mean and variance.

Solution: The sample mean is calculated from Eq. (3.2).

$$\bar{x} = \frac{1}{n} \sum x = \frac{1}{10} (10) = 1.0$$

The sample variance is calculated from Eq. (3.4).

$(x - \bar{x})$		$(x - \bar{x})^2$
$4 - 1 =$	3	9
$-18 - 1 =$	-19	361
$16 - 1 =$	15	225
$-4 - 1 =$	-5	25
$8 - 1 =$	7	49
$2 - 1 =$	1	1
$-4 - 1 =$	-5	25
$6 - 1 =$	5	25
$-10 - 1 =$	-11	121
$10 - 1 =$	9	81
		$\sum (x - \bar{x})^2 = 922$

$$s^2 = (1/n) \sum (x - \bar{x})^2 = (1/10)(922) = 92.2$$

3.3 Unbiased Estimates

The most useful function of a random sample is its ability to make estimates of the universe parameters, μ and σ^2. If a random sample is from a normal distribution, the sample mean, $\bar{x}$, is the best available estimate of the theoretical mean of the distribution, μ. If a random sample comes from a normal distribution, the universe variance σ^2, can be best estimated by the expression

$$\hat{s}^2 = \frac{1}{n-1} \sum_{i=1}^{n} (x_i - \bar{x})^2 \tag{3.5}$$

where $\hat{s}^2$ is the *unbiased estimate* of σ^2. This expression is one of the most useful parameters in the analysis of experiments.

Notice that the difference between Eqs. (3.4) and (3.5) lies in the denominator of the coefficient. It is known that the second moment about the mean of a sample has an inherent bias when used as an estimate of σ^2. It is also known that this bias is corrected by using $1/(n-1)$ in place of $1/n$ as the multiplier. This will now be proven.

Let x_i be any trial in a sample of size n. Since

$$(x_i - \mu) \equiv (x_i - \bar{x}) + (\bar{x} - \mu)$$

on squaring each side we get

$$(x_i - \mu)^2 = (x_i - \bar{x})^2 + (\bar{x} - \mu)^2 + 2(x_i - \bar{x})(\bar{x} - \mu)$$

Then, summing each side over all values, we have

$$\sum_{i=1}^{n} (x_i - \mu)^2 = \sum_{i=1}^{n} (x_i - \bar{x})^2 + n(\bar{x} - \mu)^2 + 2(\bar{x} - \mu) \sum_{i=1}^{n} (x_i - \bar{x})$$

Since we know the first moment

$$\sum_{i=1}^{n} (x_i - \bar{x})$$

to be zero by definition of $\bar{x}$, the previous expression becomes

$$\sum_{i=1}^{n} (x_i - \mu)^2 = \sum_{i=1}^{n} (x_i - \bar{x})^2 + n(\bar{x} - \mu)^2$$

For a large number of samples, the mean of the left side of the above expression will tend to $n\sigma^2$ (by definition of σ^2). The mean value of the second term on the right side of the expression will tend to $n(\sigma^2/n)$. Therefore

$$\sum_{i=1}^{n} (x_i - \bar{x})^2 + n(\sigma^2/n)$$

is an estimate of $n\sigma^2$ or

$$\sum_{i=1}^{n} (x_i - \bar{x})^2$$

is an estimate of $(n - 1)\sigma^2$ and

$$\hat{s}^2 = \frac{1}{n-1} \sum_{i=1}^{n} (x_i - \bar{x})^2$$

is an estimate of σ^2. Thus, the mean value of $\hat{s}^2$ over a large number of random samples tends to σ^2, and as n approaches ∞, $\hat{s}^2$ approaches σ^2. It is therefore said that $\hat{s}^2$ is an unbiased estimate of σ^2, confirming the statement in Eq. (3.5).

As n becomes large, the calculation of $\hat{s}^2$ in the form shown in Eq. (3.5) becomes quite laborious. To make calculations easier we will derive an alternate form. We know that

$$\sum_{i=1}^{n} (x_i - \bar{x})^2 = \sum_{i=1}^{n} (x_i^2 + \bar{x}^2 - 2x_i\bar{x}) = \sum_{i=1}^{n} x_i^2 + n\bar{x}^2 - 2\bar{x} \sum_{i=1}^{n} x_i$$

Since $\sum_{i=1}^{n} x_i = n\bar{x}$, then

$$\sum_{i=1}^{n} (x_i - \bar{x})^2 = \sum_{i=1}^{n} x_i^2 - n\bar{x}^2$$

$$= \sum_{i=1}^{n} x_i^2 - \frac{1}{n}\left(\sum_{i=1}^{n} x_i\right)^2$$

and from Eq. (3.5) we get

$$\hat{s}^2 = \frac{1}{n-1}\left[\sum_{i=1}^{n} x_i^2 - \frac{1}{n}\left(\sum_{i=1}^{n} x_i\right)^2\right] \tag{3.6}$$

giving the alternate form for easier calculation.

3.3.1 Example. In Example 3.2.1 calculate the unbiased estimate of σ^2 from the sample data using (a) the "sum of squares" method, and (b) the alternate form.

Solution:

(a) Using Eq. (3.5)

$$\hat{s}^2 = (1/n - 1) \sum_{i=1}^{n} (x_i - \bar{x})^2$$

and substituting from data in Example 3.2.1

$$\hat{s}^2 = (1/9)(922) = 102.4$$

(b) Using Eq. (3.6)

$$\hat{s}^2 = (1/n - 1)[\sum x^2 - (1/n)(\sum x)^2]$$

and substituting from data in Example 3.2.1

$$\hat{s}^2 = \tfrac{1}{9}[932 - \tfrac{1}{10}(10)^2]$$
$$= \tfrac{1}{9}[922] = 102.4$$

3.3.2 Example. For samples of large size n, $\hat{s}$ is an unbiased estimate of σ. To demonstrate the relationship between the universe value and the unbiased estimate for the standard deviation, suppose that in Example 3.3.1 the $\hat{s}^2$ was determined from a large sample. (a) What is the probability of getting a response value $x \geq 10$, as determined by universe values? (b) What is the probability using sample estimates?

Solution: (a) This part is identical to Example 2.6.2. Given that

$$\mu = 0, \quad \sigma = 10, \quad x = 10$$

we calculate the standardized normal random variable

$$z = \frac{x - \mu}{\sigma} = \frac{10 - 0}{10} = 1.0$$

From Appendix E, $P(x \geq 10) = 1 - 0.8413 = 0.1587$.

(b) In this case we substitute the sample mean $\bar{x}$ for μ and the unbiased estimate $\hat{s}$ for σ. Given that

$$\bar{x} = 1.0$$
$$\hat{s} = \sqrt{102.4} = 10.12$$
$$x = 10$$

the standardized normal variate is

$$z = \frac{x - \bar{x}}{\hat{s}} = \frac{10 - 1}{10.12} = 0.89$$

From Appendix E, $P(x \geq 10) = 1 - 0.8133 = 0.1867$.

Note: The difference between (a) 0.1587 and (b) 0.1867 is attributable to the error of estimating μ and σ by the sample values $\bar{x}$ and $\hat{s}$.)

3.4 Degrees of Freedom

In the previous section it was shown that when $n - 1$ is substituted for n, the variance calculation is an unbiased estimate of the true variance. The $(n - 1)$ term is called the *degrees of freedom*, ν, of the estimate of variance. The degrees of freedom for a particular estimate, $\hat{s}^2$, is the number of independent contrasts that can be made among the n responses. For x_1, $x_2, \ldots x_n$, there are $n - 1$ independent contrasts such as $(x_1 - x_2)$. This can be demonstrated as follows:

Given a sample, $n = 5$, with responses x_1, x_2, x_3, x_4, and x_5, the independent contrasts are

$$x_1 - x_2$$
$$x_2 - x_3$$
$$x_3 - x_4$$
$$x_4 - x_5$$

The additional contrast $(x_1 - x_5)$ is not independent since we already know its value from $(x_1 - x_2) + (x_2 - x_3) + (x_3 - x_4) + (x_4 - x_5) = (x_1 - x_5)$.

Therefore, for a sample of $n = 5$, there are four $(n - 1)$ independent contrasts or degrees of freedom. The concept is of fundamental importance and should be fully understood. When n is large, its importance is obviously diminished because $n/(n - 1)$ approaches unity as n approaches ∞. For general experimental conditions, n is often of the size that the degrees of freedom of the variance estimate is of vital importance.

3.5 Covariance

Our discussion up to this point has been restricted to the consideration of a single random variable and the calculation of its mean and variance. Suppose that two random variables, x_1 and x_2, are measured and used to calculate a third quantity by the formula

$$y = ax_1 \pm bx_2$$

where a and b are constants. Let us assume that n_1 and n_2 number of responses of x_1 and x_2 are so large that $\bar{x}_1$ and $\bar{x}_2$ become accurate estimates of μ_1 and μ_2 and hence μ is a true mean value for y. The above expression then becomes

$$\mu = a\mu_1 \pm b\mu_2 \tag{3.7}$$

If δy is the deviation of an observation from its mean then

$$\delta y = a\delta x_1 \pm b\delta x_2$$

squaring both sides

$$(\delta y)^2 = a^2(\delta x_1)^2 + b^2(\delta x_2)^2 + 2ab\delta x_1\delta x_2$$

The mean value of $(\delta x_1)^2$ is

$$\frac{(\delta x_1)^2}{n} = \frac{(x_1 - \bar{x}_1)^2}{n} = s_1^2$$

the sample variance for x_1. The same is true with s_2^2 for x_2 and s^2 for y. Thus

$$s^2 = a^2 s_1^2 + b^2 s_2^2 \pm 2ab \, \text{cov}(x_1 x_2) \tag{3.8}$$

where the last term, cov $(x_1 x_2)$, is called the *covariance* of x_1 and x_2, defined as

$$\frac{1}{n}\sum_1^n \delta x_1 \, \delta x_2 = \frac{1}{n}\sum_1^n (x_1 - \mu_1)(x_2 - \mu_2) \tag{3.9}$$

Note that the right side of Eq. (3.9) is analogous to a variance term, except that instead of being the *square* of one variable it contains the *product* of two variables. The unbiased estimate of a covariance from a sample, the true means being unknown, is given by

$$\hat{s}^2 = \frac{1}{n-1}\left(\sum_1^n x_1 x_2 - n\bar{x}_1\bar{x}_2\right) \tag{3.10}$$

written in alternate form analogous to Eq. (3.6).

If x_1 and x_2 in Eq. (3.8) are independent, then no covariance will exist. The variance of y then becomes

$$s^2 = a^2 s_1^2 + b^2 s_2^2 \tag{3.11}$$

an important and useful relationship between the variances of multiple independent random variables [9].

3.5.1 Example. If the mean and variance of one rod length are 5 in. and 1 in., respectively; and for another rod length, 10 in. and 2 in., respectively, what would be the mean and variance of the rod lengths placed end to end?

Solution:

This is a problem that combines the means and variances of two random variables when we consider that no other rods exist. From Eq. (3.7), with a and b being unity

$$\mu = \mu_1 + \mu_2$$

where

$$\mu_1 = 5 \text{ in.}, \qquad \mu_2 = 10 \text{ in.}$$

giving that

$$\mu = 5 + 10 = 15 \text{ in.}$$

This simple illustration shows the additive relationship between two means when combined.

The combined variance is determined by Eq. (3.11). Given that

$$s_1^2 = 1 \text{ in.}$$
$$s_2^2 = 2 \text{ in.}$$

then

$$s^2 = 1 \text{ in.} + 2 \text{ in.} = 3 \text{ in.}$$

3.6 Other Measures of Central Tendency

The *arithmetic mean* is given by Eq. (3.2) as

$$\bar{x} = \frac{1}{n} \sum_{i=1}^{n} x_i$$

and is known to be the first moment about the origin of a set of data. This particular average is the most commonly used measure of central tendency because it usually provides the best estimate of the most typical value in the distribution of data. There are many situations, however, when the arithmetic mean is not the best estimate of central tendency. We shall consider a few of these at this time.

3.6.1 The Median. The response occupying the middle position in a sample of data is known as the *median*. Given the responses 1, 2, 3, 4, 5 in a sample of $n = 5$, the median value is 3. In another sample of responses 0, 0, 3, 6, 10, the median would still be 3. This demonstrates an important characteristic of the median: it is unaffected by the numerical value of the other responses in the sample.

The median is a superior measure of central tendency in special situations where the data are non-normal and the distribution is quite peaked. It is also useful in providing a determination of an average for a sample of data taken from a *time-phased* variable. For example, if we wish to determine the average time-to-corrosion for a certain metal we could use the median and observe only half of the specimens. Thus, with a sample of twenty-five specimens we could measure the time-to-corrosion for the first thirteen specimens, the thirteenth then being the median time-to-corrosion. No observation of the other twelve would be necessary, thus saving the greater part of the time for observing the specimens.

Average test scores are usually median scores because the distribution of test scores is generally non-normal. The half-life measure of radioactivity is also a median average of the life of a radioactive substance. This median represents the only way of obtaining an average radioactive life since the total radioactive life is infinite.

3.6.2 The Mode. The most frequently occurring response in a sample of data is called the *modal value* or *mode*. This measure is not very meaningful unless a large size n is involved. In a histogram of data the mode would be the value that represents the highest concentration of data. For example, in Fig. 3.1, the mode is 2 since it represents the value with the largest frequency of data.

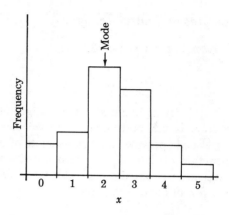

Fig. 3.1. The Mode of a Typical Histogram

If the mean and median are known for a sample of data and the data are only moderately asymmetrical, the mode can be calculated as

$$\text{Mode} = 3 \text{ Median} - 2 \text{ Mean} \tag{3.12}$$

If the distribution is symmetrical, the mean, median, and mode are equal.

3.6.3 The Geometric Mean. The geometric mean is an important average when dealing with ratios or percentages. It is defined as

$$g = \sqrt[n]{x_1 \cdot x_2 \cdot x_3 \ldots x_n} \tag{3.13}$$

or

$$\log g = \frac{\log x_1 + \log x_2 + \log x_3 + \ldots + \log x_n}{n} \tag{3.14}$$

with Eq. (3.14) being the arithmetic mean of the log of the responses.

3.6.4 Example. What is the geometric mean of the numbers 9 and 16? *Solution:* From Eq. (3.13) we have

$$g = \sqrt{x_1 \cdot x_2} = \sqrt{9 \cdot 16} = \sqrt{144} = 12.0$$

3.6.5 Harmonic Mean. Another special type of average is given by

$$H = \frac{n}{\sum\limits_{i=1}^{n} 1/x_i} \tag{3.15}$$

and is called the *harmonic mean*. It is the reciprocal of the arithmetic mean of the reciprocal of the responses and can also be written as

$$\frac{1}{H} = \frac{1}{n} \sum\limits_{i=1}^{n} 1/x_i \tag{3.16}$$

3.6.6 Example. What is the harmonic mean of the numbers 9 and 16?

Solution: From Eq. (3.15)

$$H = \frac{n}{\sum 1/x} = \frac{2}{1/9 + 1/16} = 11.5$$

3.6.7 Quadratic Mean. An important average used in electrical engineering is the *quadratic mean*. It is defined as

$$Q = \sqrt{\frac{1}{n} \sum_{i=1}^{n} x_i^2} = \text{r.m.s.} \tag{3.17}$$

where r.m.s. stands for *root mean square*. It can also be described as the *second moment* about the origin.

3.6.8 Example. What is the quadratic mean of the numbers 9 and 16?

Solution: From Eq. (3.17) we have

$$Q = \sqrt{(1/n) \sum x^2} = \sqrt{\tfrac{1}{2}[(9)^2 + (16)^2]} = 13.0$$

3.7 Other Measures of Variation

In Sec. 3.2 we observed that the variance of a sample is given by

$$s^2 = \frac{1}{n} \sum_{i=1}^{n} (x_i - \bar{x})^2 \tag{3.18}$$

and its standard deviation

$$s = \sqrt{\frac{1}{n} \sum_{i=1}^{n} (x_i - \bar{x})^2} \tag{3.19}$$

which is the root mean square, Eq. (3.17), of the deviations from the sample mean, or the second moment. There are other useful measures of variation that are important to consider even though Eqs. (3.18) and (3.19) are generally the most reliable and useful.

3.7.1 The Range. A very useful and easily calculated measure of variation is the *range*. It is simply the difference between the largest and smallest response in the sample. When n is small, the range is closely proportional to the standard deviation and is sometimes used as an easily calculated approximation.

3.7.2 Example. What is the range of the numbers 3, 6, 10, 4, 2?

Solution: The largest number is 10, the smallest is 2. Therefore,

$$Range = 10 - 2 = 8$$

3.7.3 The Average Deviation. The first moment of the absolute deviations about the mean is known as the *average deviation*. If absolute values were not used, the average deviation would always be zero (see Sec. 2.6.1). The average deviation is therefore written

$$\text{A.D.} = \frac{\sum_{i=1}^{n} |x_i - \bar{x}|}{n} \tag{3.20}$$

3.7.4   Example. Determine the average deviation of the numbers in Example 3.7.2.

Solution: Given from Eq. (3.20) we have

$$\begin{aligned}
\text{A.D.} &= \frac{\sum |x - \bar{x}|}{n} \\
&= \frac{|3 - 5| + |6 - 5| + |10 - 5| + |4 - 5| + |2 - 5|}{n} \\
&= \frac{2 + 1 + 5 + 1 + 3}{5} = 2.4
\end{aligned}$$

3.7.5   The Quartile Deviation. For distributions where the median is used as the preferred measure of central tendency, a useful measure of variation is the *quartile deviation*. It is defined by

$$Q = \frac{Q_3 - Q_1}{2} \tag{3.21}$$

where Q_1 and Q_3 are the first and third quartiles, respectively, of a set of data. The first quartile is the median value between the lowest response and the median average for the total sample. The third quartile is the median value between the sample median and the highest response in the sample.

3.7.6   Example. Determine the quartile deviation for the following data: 2, 3, 4, 5, 6, 7, 8, 9, 10.

Solution: The median of the data is 6. Therefore, the first quartile (Q_1) is the middle value between 2 and 6, which is 4. Q_3 is the middle value between 6 and 10, which is 8. Therefore, from Eq. (3.21)

$$Q = \frac{Q_3 - Q_1}{2} = \frac{8 - 4}{2} = 2.0$$

3.8   The Distribution of a Sample Mean

We have thus far limited our study of distributions to those that relate to the characteristics of samples consisting of individual trials or responses. Suppose that in Table 3.1 we calculated the mean for each sample thus:

$$\frac{\sum_{i=1}^{n} x_{1i}}{n} = \bar{x}_1, \quad \frac{\sum_{i=1}^{n} x_{2i}}{n} = \bar{x}_2, \quad \frac{\sum_{i=1}^{n} x_{ki}}{n} = \bar{x}_k$$

giving k number of sample means. We will now determine the distribution of the variable $\bar{x}_{ij}$, with $i = 1, 2, 3, \ldots, n$ responses per sample and $j = 1, 2, 3, \ldots, k$ samples.

To find the frequency function of a sample mean, $\bar{x}$, we will consider its moment generating function. To do so, we must first observe some properties of such functions.

If $g(x)$ is any function for which the moment generating function exists, and c is any constant, then

$$M_{cg(x)}(\Theta) = M_{g(x)}(c\Theta) \tag{3.22}$$

and

$$M_{g(x)+c}(\Theta) = e^{c\Theta}M_{g(x)}(\Theta) \tag{3.23}$$

Given, also, that the moment generating function of the sum of n independent variables is equal to the product of the moment generating function of the individual variables, that is,

$$M_{x_1+x_2+\cdots+x_n}(\Theta) = M_{x_1}(\Theta)M_{x_2}(\Theta) \ldots M_{x_n}(\Theta) \tag{3.24}$$

therefore, knowing Eq. (3.22), it follows that

$$M_{\bar{x}}(\Theta) = M_{(x_1+x_2+\cdots+x_n)/n}(\Theta) = M_{x_1+x_2+\cdots+x_n}(\Theta/n) \tag{3.25}$$

and from Eq. (3.24), Equation (3.25) becomes

$$M_{\bar{x}}(\Theta) = M_{x_1}(\Theta/n)M_{x_2}(\Theta/n) \ldots M_{x_n}(\Theta/n) \tag{3.26}$$

Given that $x_1, x_2 \ldots x_n$ are random variables, then

$$f(x_1) = f(x_2) = f(x_n)$$

and from Eq. (3.26) we write

$$M_{\bar{x}}(\Theta) = M_x^n(\Theta/n) \tag{3.27}$$

Now, from Eq. (2.37), we can write

$$M_{x-\mu_x}(\Theta) = e^{(1/2)\Theta^2\sigma_x^2} \tag{3.28}$$

Therefore, by using Eq. (3.23) in Eq. (3.28) it follows that

$$M_x(\Theta) = e^{\mu_x\Theta}M_{x-\mu}(\Theta) = e^{\mu_x\Theta + (1/2)\,\Theta^2\sigma_x^2} \tag{3.29}$$

and by replacing Θ with Θ/n, Eqs. (3.27) and (3.29) will give

$$M_{\bar{x}}(\Theta) = [e^{\mu_x\Theta/n + (1/2)(\Theta/n)^2\sigma_x^2}]^n = e^{\mu_x\Theta + (1/2)\Theta^2(\sigma_x^2/n)} \tag{3.30}$$

which is the moment generating function of a normal variable $(\bar{x})$ with mean μ_x and standard deviation $\sigma_x/\sqrt{n}$. Since a moment generating function uniquely determines a frequency function, we can conclude from Eq. (3.30) that a sample mean $\bar{x}$ is normally distributed with mean μ and standard deviation $\sigma/\sqrt{n}$. This standard deviation term, $\sigma/\sqrt{n}$, is more commonly known as the *standard error of the mean*.

The applications of statistical method would be restricted indeed if this normally distributed characteristic of sample means was true only for those drawn from normal distributions. Many phenomena are not normally distributed, and therefore, if such a restriction on the distribution of means did exist, many of the methods of interpretation would be invalid. It can be proven, however, that as $n \to \infty$ in a sample, the sample mean $\bar{x}$ and standard deviation sample s approach μ and σ, respectively, as a normal distribution with the standard error of the mean, $\sigma_{\bar{x}}$, given by $\sigma/\sqrt{n}$.

3.8.1 Example. This characteristic of sample means will now be demonstrated by an example. Suppose that we assign the number *zero* to an occurrence of heads on a coin and the number *one* to the occurrence of tails on a coin. We can therefore assign numerical values to the expectancies of heads and tails in three tosses of a coin as summarized in Table 2.2, page 11. If we consider these values to be responses drawn from a variable x (with a non-normal distribution) and each group of tosses as a sample of $n = 3$, we would then have k samples ($k = 8$) of $n = 3$ responses in each sample. These data are summarized in Table 3.3.

TABLE 3.3

Data from Three Tosses of Coin in Table 2.2

Samples	Toss (x Response) 1	2	3	x_i	$\bar{x}_i$	$\bar{x}_i^2$
x_1	0 (H)	0 (H)	0 (H)	0	0	0
x_2	0 (H)	0 (H)	1 (T)	1	1/3	1/9
x_3	0 (H)	1 (T)	1 (T)	2	2/3	4/9
x_4	1 (T)	1 (T)	1 (T)	3	3/3	1
x_5	1 (T)	1 (T)	0 (H)	2	2/3	4/9
x_6	1 (T)	0 (H)	0 (H)	1	1/3	1/9
x_7	1 (T)	0 (H)	1 (T)	2	2/3	4/9
x_8	0 (H)	1 (T)	0 (H)	1	1/3	1/9
Column Totals				12	4	8/3

These data can also be the expected result of 24 tosses of a single coin or a single sample with $N = n \times k = 24$. In such a case we calculate the mean as

$$\mu_x = \frac{\sum x}{N} = \frac{0 + 0 + \ldots + 0 + 1}{24} = \frac{12}{24} = \frac{1}{2} \tag{3.31}$$

and the variance as

$$\sigma_x^2 = \frac{\sum x^2 - \frac{(\sum x)^2}{N}}{N} = \frac{12 - \frac{(12)^2}{24}}{24} = 1/4 \qquad (3.32)$$

with universe values, μ_x and σ_x^2, used because the twenty-four responses constitute the entire universe of values.

When Eq. (3.30) is true, we can expect

$$\mu_{\bar{x}} = \mu_x \qquad (3.33)$$

and

$$\sigma_{\bar{x}}^2 = \frac{\sigma_x^2}{n} \qquad (3.34)$$

To test these statements we return to Table 3.3 and calculate $\mu_{\bar{x}}$ as the mean of the sample means or

$$\mu_{\bar{x}} = \frac{\sum_{i=1}^{n} \bar{x}_i}{k} = 4/8 = 1/2 \quad (k = \text{number of samples}) \qquad (3.35)$$

which is the same as in Eq. (3.31), thus confirming Eq. (3.32) to be true. Further, we can calculate from data in Table 3.3 the quantity

$$\sigma_{\bar{x}}^2 = \frac{\sum_{i=1}^{n} \bar{x}^2 - \frac{\left(\sum_{i=1}^{n} \bar{x}_i\right)^2}{k}}{k} = \frac{8/3 - (4)^2/8}{8} = 1/12 \qquad (3.36)$$

and if we set Eq. (3.34) equal to Eq. (3.36), we have

$$\frac{\sigma_x^2}{n} = 1/12$$

or

$$n = 12\sigma_x^2$$

and from Eq. (3.32) we substitute and get

$$n = 12(1/4) = 3 \qquad (3.37)$$

the size of a sample x_i. We can also write the standard error of the mean as

$$\sigma_{\bar{x}} = \sigma_x/\sqrt{n} \qquad (3.38)$$

With $\sigma_x = \sqrt{1/4}$ and $n = 3$ we substitute in Eq. (3.38) and get

$$\sigma_{\bar{x}} = \sqrt{1/4}/\sqrt{3} = 1/\sqrt{12} \qquad (3.39)$$

which is seen to be the square root of $\sigma_{\bar{x}}^2$.

The standard error of the mean in Eq. (3.38) is therefore the standard deviation of a normal distribution, which is the form of Eq. (2.40), page 31, and for the distribution of $\bar{x}$, we therefore are given

$$f(\bar{x}) = (1/\sqrt{2\pi})\, e^{-z^2/2} \tag{3.40}$$

where

$$z = \frac{(\bar{x} - \mu)}{\sigma/\sqrt{n}} \tag{3.41}$$

giving an expression for μ and $\sigma_{\bar{x}}$ in standardized form. From Eq. (3.40) the integral becomes

$$P\left(\bar{x} > \frac{\bar{x} - \mu}{\sigma/\sqrt{n}}\right) = \int_{\frac{\bar{x}-\mu}{\sigma/\sqrt{n}}}^{\infty} (1/\sqrt{2\pi})\, e^{-z^2/2}\, dz = \alpha \tag{3.42}$$

where α represents the excluded area under the curve.

We can conclude then that if x has a distribution with mean μ and standard deviation σ for which the moment generating function exists, the variable

$$z = \frac{(\bar{x} - \mu)}{\sigma/\sqrt{n}}$$

has a distribution that approaches the standard normal distribution as $n \to \infty$. This conclusion is known as the *central limit theorem*. This theorem gives emphasis to the importance of the normal distribution that was derived in Chapter 2.

3.9 Exercises   (*Note:* Refer to Appendix D, Page 170, for data sets.)

3.1. Toss three coins eight times and tabulate the number of heads on each toss. (a) Construct a histogram of your results. (b) Construct the expected histogram for this case. (c) Compare your results in (a) and (b).

3.2. Toss three coins forty times and tabulate the number of heads on each toss. (a) Construct a histogram of your results. (b) Construct the expected histogram. (c) Compare your results. (d) Compare your results with those in 3.1.

3.3. For data set 1c, what percentage of all the participants inserted the first tube in (a) 0.30 minutes or less? (b) more than 0.48 minutes? (c) between 0.18 and 0.49 minutes?

3.4. For data set 1d, calculate the probability of a participant completing the assigned task in (a) 0.60 minutes or less, (b) greater than 2.00 minutes, (c) between 1.00 and 2.00 minutes.

3.5. Plot the histograms for data set 1c and data set 1d. Discuss the difference between the two histograms.

3.6. What is the arithmetic mean of two 2's, three 3's, and four 4's?

3.7. What is the arithmetic mean of the first column of data in data set 1a? The second column?

3.8. What is the standard deviation of the data in Exercise 3.6? In Exercise 3.7?

3.9. Calculate the mean and standard deviation for data set 1a and for data set 1b.

3.10. Calculate the unbiased estimate of σ^2 from the first 25 observations (read vertically) of data set 1a by (a) the "sum of squares" method, (b) the alternate form.

3.11. Prove that $n - 1$ independent contrasts exist for a sample size of 9.

3.12. Given the first 25 observations (read vertically) of data set 1a, calculate the first, second, and third moments (a) about the origin, (b) about the mean.

3.13. With respect to the first five observations (read vertically) of data set 1a and the first five observations (read vertically) of data set 1b, estimate (a) the variance of each, (b) the standard deviation of each, (c) the covariance.

3.14. For data set 2, what is the covariance between x_1 and x_2?

3.15. Write the terms in each of the following summations.

(a) $\sum_{i=0}^{3} (i)$ (b) $\sum_{i=1}^{3} (x_i + 3)$ (c) $\left(\sum_{j=1}^{4} x_j \right)^2$

(d) $\sum_{i=1}^{4} (y_i^2 + i)$ (e) $\sum_{k=1}^{n} (z_k^2 + 2)$ (f) $\sum_{j=1}^{4} x_j^2$ (g) $\sum_{i=1}^{n} \sum_{j=1}^{k} x_{ij}$

3.16. Write each of the following in summation notation.

(a) $1 + 3 + 5$

(b) $(y_1 + 4) + (y_2 + 4)^2 + (y_3 + 4)^3$

(c) $(A_1 - B) + (A_2 - B) + (A_3 - B) + \ldots + (A_n - B)$

(d) $x_1 y_1 + x_2 y_2 + x_3 y_3 + \ldots + x_n y_n$

(e) $(x_1 + x_2 + x_3 + \ldots + x_n)(y_1 + y_2 + y_3 + \ldots + y_n)$

3.17. What is the median of the data in Exercise 3.7? Compare with the arithmetic mean.

3.18. What are the modal classes for data sets 1c and 1d?

3.19. What is the geometric mean of the numbers (a) 4 and 9, (b) 3, 5, and 7?

3.20. For Exercise 3.19, what is the harmonic mean?

3.21. For Exercise 3.19, what is the quadratic mean or root mean square?

3.22. What is the range for the data in Exercise 3.7?

3.23. What is the average deviation of the data in (a) Exercise 3.6, and (b) Exercise 3.7?

3.24. What is the quartile deviation for the data in Exercise 3.7?

3.25. What is the standard error of the mean in (a) Exercise 3.6, (b) Exercise 3.7, (c) Exercise 3.9?

3.26. If x is normally distributed with $\mu = 2.00$ and $\sigma = 0.65$, what is the probability that a sample of size $n = 16$ will have a mean (a) > 2.00, (b) < 1.95, (c) > 2.10?

3.27. Plot the distribution function $F(x)$ (Appendix B) for data set 1c and 1d. Compare the two distributions.

CHAPTER 4

Analysis of Experiments
with One Independent Variable

In Chapter 3 we observed the characteristics and use of samples in the experimental process. We will now consider the methods of analyzing experimental data when it is desirable to measure and describe a given phenomenon.

When a random sample is drawn from a given random variable without any reference to sublevels of the variable, it can be said that the levels of the variable are *not predetermined* in the experiment. The phenomenon that is being investigated is either allowed to function freely without limitations or, in many cases, there is no choice but to allow such limitations to occur. In Example 3.2.1 the random sample of $n = 10$ responses drawn from a normal distribution illustrates such a case. A more specific example would be a case in which temperature is the independent random variable. To draw a random sample of temperature responses without restriction would be a case of an experiment with unpredetermined levels.

In other types of experiments it is either desirable or necessary to classify a variable at different functional levels. These levels of a variable may be *predetermined* in two basic ways: One way would be to classify the original variable into sublevels. In the temperature example above, the full range of temperature, say 0 to 100 degrees centigrade, could be divided into sublevels such as 0 to 25, 26 to 50, 51 to 75, 76 to 100 degrees. There are other cases in which the variable is inherently predetermined at sublevels. Such variables are, by their nature, expressed as discrete units and cannot be measured on a continuous numerical scale. Variables such as machines, alloys, or operators are of this type.

This experimental condition, the predetermined characteristic of the independent variable, is an important criterion in both the analysis and interpretation of experimental results.

4.1 Level of Variable Not Predetermined

We have already observed that a given theoretical frequency function can be estimated by drawing from it a random sample. We can illustrate this with a diagram,

$$\boxed{\begin{array}{c}\text{Theoretical}\\\text{Distribution}\end{array}}-f(x)\rightarrow\boxed{\begin{array}{c}\text{Random}\\\text{Sample}\end{array}}-x_i\rightarrow$$

where x_i represents the ith independent trial (where $i = 1, 2, \ldots n$) from the frequency function $f(x)$. If for the ith trial we draw the ith response, y_i, we would then have

$$\boxed{\begin{array}{c}\text{Theoretical}\\\text{Distribution}\end{array}}-f(x)\rightarrow\boxed{\begin{array}{c}\text{Random}\\\text{Sample}\end{array}}-x_i\rightarrow\boxed{\begin{array}{c}\text{The}\\\text{Experiment}\end{array}}-y_i\rightarrow$$

The input-output data for the experiment would be as shown in Table 4.1.

The relationship between the variables can be further explained by the mathematical model

$$y_i = \mu + \tau_i + \varepsilon_i$$

where y_i represents the ith response on the ith trial of x_i, and μ represents the *common effect* contained by the total experiment. τ_i is the *real effect* of the ith level of the random variable x. The ε_i represents the *random error* in the ith response, whose mean is zero and whose variance is the same for all responses.

4.1.1 Linear Regression. The amount of the variation in the dependent variable (y) that can be explained by the variance of the independent variable (x) is known as the *regression* of y upon x. If this dependence is linear it is called *linear regression*. The linear relationship between a dependent variable y and an independent variable x is known to be

$$y_i = \beta_0 + \beta_1 x_i + \varepsilon_i \tag{4.1}$$

TABLE 4.1

General Sample Data for an Experiment

Trial Number	Independent Variable (x)	Dependent Variable (y)
1	x_1	y_1
2	x_2	y_2
.	.	.
.	.	.
.	.	.
.	.	.
i	x_i	x_i
.	.	.
.	.	.
.	.	.
n	x_n	y_n

where β_0 is the intercept of the y axis by the *true* linear regression line and β_1 is the slope of this true line. The term ε_i represents the random error present in the regression of y and x. It is the amount of the variance in y that *cannot* be attributed to the variance in x. This latter term, as before, is considered to be a normally and independently distributed random variable whose mean value is zero and whose variance is the same for all levels.

For a given experimental situation it is necessary to estimate β_0 and β_1 from an empirical sample of data. The most useful method for making such estimates is known as the "method of least squares" and will be derived at this time [9]. Let a line AB represent any estimated linear relationship between x and y. Let (x_i, y_i) be any given response (see Fig. 4.1), with b_0 and b_1 being the intercept and slope, respectively, of estimated line AB. Thus, b_0 and b_1 become estimates of β_0 and β_1.

If line AB is used to estimate y_i from x_i, from Eq. (4.1) we can write

$$y_i' = b_0 + b_1 x_i \tag{4.2}$$

the expression for the regression estimate (y_i') of y_i for a given x_i. The difference between the estimated value (y_i') and the actual value (y_i) is, from Eqs. (4.2) and (4.1), the estimated error (e_i) in the ith response; thus,

$$e_i = y_i - y_i' = y_i - (b_0 + b_1 x_i) \tag{4.3}$$

We will now demonstrate that the line of best fit is the line that is determined when the sum of squares of the differences are at a minimum.

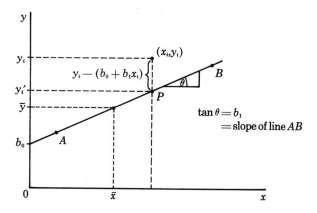

Fig. 4.1. An Estimated Linear Relationship

Since Eq. (4.3) can be positive or negative, the complexity of calculation is avoided by squaring the terms in Eq. (4.3); thus,

$$e_i^2 = [y_i - (b_0 + b_1 x_i)]^2$$

and the sum of squares of these for all the points become

$$\sum_{i=1}^{n} e_i^2 = \sum_{i=1}^{n} [y_i - (b_0 + b_1 x_i)]^2$$

Values for b_0 and b_1 are now determined to make $\sum_{i=1}^{n} e_i^2$ a *minimum* by differentiating partially with respect to b_0 and b_1, separately, setting equal to zero, and solving for b_0 and b_1. Thus,

$$\frac{\partial}{\partial b_0}\left(\sum_{i=1}^{n} e_i^2\right) = -2 \sum_{i=1}^{n} [y_i - (b_0 + b_1 x_i)] = 0$$

$$\frac{\partial}{\partial b_1}\left(\sum_{i=1}^{n} e_i^2\right) = -2 \sum_{i=1}^{n} x_i[y_i - (b_0 + b_1 x_i)] = 0$$

gives

$$\sum_{i=1}^{n} y_i = nb_0 + b_1 \sum_{i=1}^{n} x_i \tag{4.4}$$

$$\sum_{i=1}^{n} x_i y_i = b_0 \sum_{i=1}^{n} x_i + b_1 \sum_{i=1}^{n} x_i^2 \tag{4.5}$$

where n is the number of responses. From Eq. (4.4) we get

$$b_0 = \frac{1}{n} \sum_{i=1}^{n} y_i - \frac{b_1}{n} \sum_{i=1}^{n} x_i$$

$$b_0 = \bar{y} - b_1 \bar{x} \tag{4.6}$$

where $\bar{y}$ = mean of y_i values, and $\bar{x}$ = mean of x_i values. Observe that the best line of fit passes through the mean of x_i and y_i.

Substituting Eq. (4.6) in Eq. (4.5), we get

$$b_1 = \left(\sum_{i=1}^{n} x_i y_i - n\bar{x}\bar{y} \right) \Big/ \left(\sum_{i=1}^{n} x_i^2 - n\bar{x}^2 \right) \tag{4.7}$$

This quantity b_1, is the estimated regression coefficient of y upon x. With the calculation of b_0 and b_1 from a given sample n, we can substitute in Eq. (4.2) and provide a regression estimate (y_i') for any assumed value for the variable x. The interpretation of such an analysis will be considered in Chapter 7.

4.1.2   Example. For eight responses of an independent variable x we obtained the following responses for a dependent variable y:

TABLE 4.2
Data Pertaining to Example 4.1.2

Response Number	x_i	y_i
1	6	4
2	1	1
3	14	9
4	8	5
5	3	2
6	11	8
7	9	7
8	4	4

What is the regression estimate for y when $x = 7$?

Solution: Calculate the following summation terms:

x	y	x^2	xy
6	4	36	24
1	1	1	1
14	9	196	126
8	5	64	40
3	2	9	6
11	8	121	88
9	7	81	63
4	4	16	16
$\sum x = 56$	$\sum y = 40$	$\sum x^2 = 524$	$\sum xy = 364$
$\bar{x} = 7,$	$\bar{y} = 5$		

From Eq. (4.7) we calculate the regression coefficient

$$b_1 = \frac{\sum xy - n\bar{x}\bar{y}}{\sum x^2 - n\bar{x}^2} = \frac{364 - 8(7)(5)}{524 - 8(7)^2} = \frac{84}{132} = 0.636$$

and from Eq. (4.6) we calculate the intercept

$$b_0 = \bar{y} - b_1\bar{x} = 5 - 0.636(7) = 0.548$$

giving the linear regression from (4.2)

$$y' = b_0 + b_1 x = 0.548 + 0.636x$$

For $x = 7$:

$$y' = 0.548 + 0.636(7) = 5.0$$

4.1.3 Example. Ten specimens of copper wire were evaluated for hardness. Each of these specimens was then given a tensile test. The results are shown in Table 4.3.

TABLE 4.3

Test Results for Ten Specimens of Copper Wire

Tensile Strength (psi)	Brinell Hardness Number
37,100	104.1
37,600	104.5
33,200	101.4
33,900	102.1
35,100	103.0
40,600	105.9
39,500	105.2
38,900	104.2
40,400	106.1
39,900	105.6

Calculate the linear regression between hardne s and tensile strength as estimated from the above sample.

Solution: Let: $x = $ hardness of copper wire

$y = $ tensile strength of copper wire

The following is calculated from above data. (Code the y values by subtracting 33,000. Code the x values by subtracting 100.)

x	$x - 100$	y	$y - 33,000$
104.1	4.1	37,100	4,100
104.5	4.5	37,600	4,600
101.4	1.4	33,200	200
102.1	2.1	33,900	900
103.0	3.0	35,100	2,100
105.9	5.9	40,600	7,600
105.2	5.2	39,500	6,500
104.2	4.2	38,900	5,900
106.1	6.1	40,400	7,400
105.6	5.6	39,900	6,900

The terms needed for solution of the simultaneous equations are calculated below:

	x	y	x^2	y^2	xy
1	4.1	4,100	16.81	16,810,000	16,810.0
2	4.5	4,600	20.25	21,160,000	20,700.0
3	1.4	200	1.96	40,000	280.0
4	2.1	900	4.41	810,000	1,890.0
5	3.0	2,100	9.00	4,410,000	6,300.0
6	5.9	7,600	34.81	57,760,000	44,840.0
7	5.2	6,500	27.04	42,250,000	33,800.0
8	4.2	5,900	17.64	34,810,000	24,780.0
9	6.1	7,400	37.21	54,760,000	45,140.0
10	5.6	6,900	31.36	47,610,000	38,640.0
Σ	42.1	46,200	200.49	280,420,000	233,180.0

$\bar{x} = 4.21$; $\bar{y} = 4620$ (*Note:* This is coded $\bar{x}$ & $\bar{y}$.)

$4.21 + 100 = 104.21$; $4,620 + 33,000 = 37,620$

Calculate the regression coefficient from Eq. (4.7)

$$b_1 = \frac{\sum xy - n\bar{x}\bar{y}}{\sum x^2 - n\bar{x}^2} = \frac{233,180.0 - (10)(4.21)(4,620)}{200.49 - (10)(4.21)(4.21)}$$

$$b_1 = \frac{233,180 - 194,502}{200.49 - 177.2} = \frac{38,678.0}{23.249}$$

$$b_1 = 1,663.64$$

Calculate the intercept from Eq. (4.6)

$$b_0 = \bar{y} - b_1(\bar{x})$$
$$= 4,620 - (1,663.64)(4.21)$$
$$= 4,620 - 7,004 = -2,384.$$

Therefore, from Eq. (4.2) we have

$$y' = b_0 + b_1 x = -2,384 + 1,663.64x \quad \text{(coded)}$$

Notice that this equation is correct when x and y are coded. For a Brinell hardness of 102, we use $x = 2$, $(102 - 100)$, and calculate a y value (943) to which 33,000 must be added to obtain the original tensile strength in psi (33,943). The regression can be transformed back to the original units by writing the coded equation as

$$y' - 33,000 = -2,384 + 1,663.64 \, (x - 100)$$
$$y' = -135,748 + 1,663.64x \text{ (in original units)}$$

Notice that the slope of the regression line is unaffected by the coding technique.

The graph of this regression line with the actual data points is shown in Fig. 4.2.

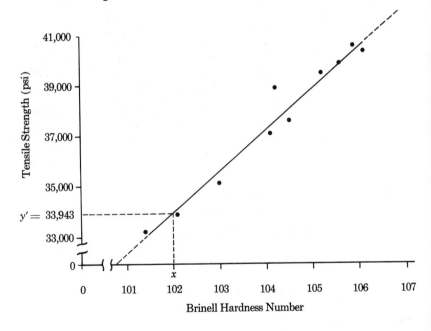

Fig. 4.2. Linear Regression of Tensile Strength on Hardness

For a Brinell hardness of $x = 102$, we substitute in the above equation

$$y' = -135,748 + 1,663.64 \, (102)$$
$$= 33,943 \text{ psi}$$

This regression value is shown on Fig. 4.2, corresponding to $x =$

102. Notice that the regression line is shown as a dash for Brinell numbers below 101.4 and above 106.1. To make predictions outside the range of the original data is to commit errors of extrapolation and therefore should be avoided.

4.1.4   Analysis of Regression Variance. The previous discussion was concerned with the method for making estimates of β_0 and β_1, the intercept and slope, so that a linear regression estimate may be calculated for a given response of x. We have already observed in Chapter 3 that such estimating with samples is subject to error. We will now be concerned with the analysis of variance in regression.

The numerator of Eq. (4.7) can be recognized as the sum of squares of the covariance (Sec. 3.5) of x_i and y_i. The denominator is the sum of square of the x's about their mean, $\bar{x}$, generally called the *sum of squares* of x. From Eq. (4.7) we can then rewrite

$$b_1 = \sum_{i=1}^{n} (x_i - \bar{x})(y_i - \bar{y}) \Big/ \sum_{i=1}^{n} (x_i - \bar{x})^2 \qquad \textbf{(4.8)}$$

Remembering that $\bar{y}$ is always on the regression line, for any given observation (x_i, y_i), the deviation of y_i from the estimated regression line can be expressed as the difference between its deviation from the mean of y and the deviation of the regression value y_i' from y_i (Fig. 4.1), giving the identity

$$y_i - y_i' \equiv (y_i - \bar{y}) - (y_i' - \bar{y})$$

The sum of squares of the deviations of the observed values of y from the line is therefore

$$\sum_{i=1}^{n} e_i^2 = \sum_{i=1}^{n} (y_i - y_i')^2 = \sum_{i=1}^{n} [(y_i - \bar{y}) - (y_i' - \bar{y})]^2$$

Expanded it gives

$$\sum_{i=1}^{n} e_i^2 = \sum_{i=1}^{n} (y_i - \bar{y})^2 - 2 \sum_{i=1}^{n} (y_i - \bar{y})(y_i' - \bar{y}) + \sum_{i=1}^{n} (y_i' - \bar{y})^2 \quad \textbf{(4.9)}$$

By substituting Eq. (4.6) in Eq. (4.2), we get

$$y_i' - \bar{y} = b_1(x_i - \bar{x}) \qquad \textbf{(4.10)}$$

and by substituting Eq. (4.10) in Eq. (4.8), we get

$$\sum_{i=1}^{n} (y_i' - \bar{y})^2 = \sum_{i=1}^{n} (y_i' - \bar{y})(y_i - \bar{y})$$

Substituting the above in Eq. (4.9), we get

$$\sum_{i=1}^{n} e_i^2 = \sum_{i=1}^{n} (y_i - \bar{y})^2 - \sum_{i=1}^{n} (y_i' - \bar{y})^2 \qquad \textbf{(4.11)}$$

giving the sum of squares of the error about the regression. The first part of the right side of Eq. (4.11) is the total sum of squares of the y responses about their mean, and the second part is the sum of squares of the predicted regression value about the mean. This latter term is known as the *sum of squares due to regression*. From Eq. (4.10) this term can be rewritten

$$\sum_{i=1}^{n} (y_i' - \bar{y})^2 = b_1^2 \sum_{i=1}^{n} (x_i - \bar{x})^2 \qquad \textbf{(4.12)}$$

The above terms are summarized in Table 4.4.

TABLE 4.4

General Analysis of Regression Variance

Source of Variation	Sum of Squares (S.S.)	Degrees of Freedom (ν)
Due to Regression	$b_1^2 \sum_{i=1}^{n} (x_i - \bar{x})^2$	1
About the Regression	$\sum_{i=1}^{n} (y_i - \bar{y})^2 - b_1^2 \sum_{i=1}^{n} (x_i - \bar{x})^2$	$n-2$
Total	$\sum_{i=1}^{n} (y_i - \bar{y})^2$	$n-1$

Table 4.4 partitions the total variation of y into that portion due to regression upon x and that portion attributable to other causes (*about the regression*). Note that the degrees of freedom (ν) are calculated as before. For variation due to regression between *two* variables, the degrees of freedom are $(2 - 1) = 1$. For degrees of freedom about regression, each set of n observations contains one contrast that is not independent, giving $n - 1 - 1$ or $n - 2$ when two variables are involved.

The unbiased estimate

$$\hat{s}^2 = \frac{\sum_{i=1}^{n} (y_i - \bar{y})^2}{n - 1}$$

of the true variance from Eq. (3.5) can also be written as

$$\hat{s}^2 = \frac{\text{Sum of Squares of } y}{\text{Degrees of Freedom}} = \text{S.S.}/\nu$$

An unbiased estimate of the regression variances can be calculated the same way. The more general term for this estimate is the *mean square* and is defined as

$$\text{M.S.} = \text{S.S.}/\nu$$

These general calculations are shown in Table 4.5, with the sum of squares terms in Table 4.4 rewritten in alternate form for ease of calculation. Such a table is called an *ANOVA* (Analysis of Variance) table.

TABLE 4.5

General ANOVA Table for Regression Variance

Source of Variation	S.S.	(ν)	M.S.
Due to Regression	$b_1^2 \left[\sum_{i=1}^{n} x_i^2 - \frac{1}{n} \left(\sum_{i=1}^{n} x_i \right)^2 \right]$	1	S.S./1
About the Regression	$\left[\sum_{i=1}^{n} y_i^2 - \frac{1}{n} \left(\sum_{i=1}^{n} y_i \right)^2 \right]$ $- b_1^2 \left[\sum_{i=1}^{n} x_i^2 - \frac{1}{n} \left(\sum_{i=1}^{n} x_i \right)^2 \right]$	$n-2$	S.S./$(n-2)$
Total	$\sum_{i=1}^{n} y_i^2 - \frac{1}{n} \left(\sum_{i=1}^{n} y_i \right)^2$	$n-1$	

The summary in Table 4.5 represents the general analysis of the linear regression variances for an experiment with a single dependent variable. The interpretation of these results will be covered in Chapters 7 and 8.

4.1.5 Example. In Example 4.1.2, calculate the sum of squares for the sources of variation and construct an ANOVA table.

Solution: (From Example 4.1.2):

$$b_1 = 0.636 \qquad \sum x = 56 \qquad n = 8$$
$$\sum x^2 = 524 \qquad \sum y = 40$$

The term $\sum y^2$ must be calculated, since it was not required previously.

y	y^2
4	16
1	1
9	81
5	25
2	4
8	64
7	49
4	16
	$\sum y^2 = 256$

The degrees of freedom for S.S. about regression are $n - 2 = 8 - 2 = 6$. From Table 4.5,

$$\text{S.S.}_{\text{total}} = \sum y^2 - (1/n)(\sum y)^2 = 256 - (1/8)(40)^2 = 56$$
$$\text{S.S.}_{\text{due to regression}} = b_1^2[\sum x^2 - (1/n)(\sum x)^2]$$
$$= (0.636)^2[524 - (1/8)(56)^2] = 53.3$$
$$\text{S.S.}_{\text{about regression}} = 56 - 53.3 = 2.7$$

TABLE 4.6
Analysis of Variance Table for Example 4.1.5

Source	S.S.	ν	M.S.
Due to Regression	53.3	1	53.3
About Regression	2.7	6	0.45
Total	56.0	7	

4.1.6 Example. In Example 4.1.3, calculate the unbiased estimate of the variance in tensile strength that can be attributed to the variance in hardness.

Solution: (From Example 4.1.3):

$$n = 10$$
$$b_1 = 1,663.64$$
$$\sum x^2 = 200.49$$
$$\sum y^2 = 280,420,000$$
$$\sum x = 42.1$$
$$\sum y = 46,200$$

Calculate sums of squares from Table 4.5.

$$\text{S.S.}_{\text{total}} = \sum y^2 - (1/n)(\sum y)^2$$
$$= 280,420,000 - \tfrac{1}{10}(46,200)^2$$
$$= 280,420,000 - 213,444,000$$
$$= 66,976,000$$

$$\text{S.S.}_{\text{reg.}} = b_1^2[\sum x^2 - (1/n)(\sum x)^2]$$
$$= (1,663.64)^2[200.49 - \tfrac{1}{10}(42.1)^2]$$
$$= 64,348,979.66$$

$$\text{S.S.}_{\text{abt. reg.}} = [\sum y^2 - (1/n)(\sum y)^2] - b_1^2[\sum x^2 - (1/n)(\sum x)^2]$$
$$= 66,976,000 - 64,348,979.66$$
$$= 2,627,020.34$$

giving the following ANOVA table:

Source	S.S.	ν	M.S.
Due to Regression	64,348,979.66	1	$\dfrac{64,348,979.66}{1} = 64,348,979.66$
About Regression	2,627,020.34	8	$\dfrac{2,627,020.34}{8} = 328,377.54$
Total	66,976,000.00	9	

4.1.7 Curvilinear Regression. Our discussion thus far has been limited to the analysis of one independent variable and its *linear* relationship to the dependent variable. Such an analysis will quite often not produce a satisfactory estimate for the problem at hand. This situation is illustrated in Fig. 4.3. Note that the linear regression line A is not adequate to de-

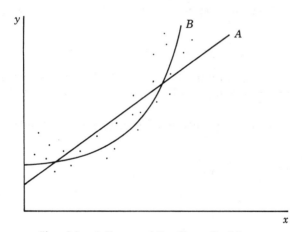

Fig. 4.3. A Linear and Curvilinear Fit of Data

scribe the trend of the data even though it may be determined by the method of least squares. A line of type B serves as a better fit of the data in such cases. When such is true, it is often of interest to explore an equation of higher order in hopes of improving the prediction of y_i values from x_i values. To do so we can expand Eq. (4.1) in general form to higher orders as

$$y_i = \beta_0 + \beta_1 x_i + \beta_2 x_i^2 + \ldots + \beta_p x_i^p + \varepsilon_i \qquad (4.13)$$

for an equation with p-order relationship. As before, $\beta_0, \beta_1, \beta_2, \ldots, \beta_p$ cannot be exactly known and must be estimated from a sample. Therefore, an estimate of any p-order regression of y on x is expressed by

$$y_i' = b_0 + b_1 x_i + b_2 x_i^2 + \ldots + b_p x_i^p \tag{4.14}$$

Since observed values will not usually satisfy this exactly, we will again use the method of least squares to estimate the b_p values. We must choose values of the b's that will minimize

$$\sum_{i=1}^{n} e_i^2 = \sum_{i=1}^{n} (y_i - y_i')^2$$

and for this particular case, from Eq. (4.14),

$$\sum_{i=1}^{n} e_i^2 = \sum_{i=1}^{n} (y_i - b_0 - b_1 x_i - b_2 x_i^2 - \ldots - b_p x_i^p)^2$$

By differentiating with respect to b_0 and equating to zero, we obtain

$$\partial/\partial b_0 \left(\sum_{i=1}^{n} e_i^2 \right) = -2 \sum_{i=1}^{n} (y_i - b_0 - b_1 x_i - b_2 x_i^2 - \ldots - b_p x_i^p) = 0$$

thus

$$nb_0 = \sum_{i=1}^{n} y_i - b_1 \sum_{i=1}^{n} x_i - b_2 \sum_{i=1}^{n} x_i^2 - \ldots - b_p \sum_{i=1}^{n} x_i^p$$

or

$$b_0 = \bar{y} - b_1 \bar{x} - b_2 \overline{x^2} - \ldots - b_p \overline{x^p} \tag{4.15}$$

where $\overline{x^p}$ is read as the mean value of x_i^p. Equation (4.15) is a general form for calculating the intercept b_0 for a p-order regression relationship between y and x.

Similarly, we develop equations for calculating any k-order coefficient, b_k. For $k \neq 0$

$$\frac{\partial}{\partial b_k} \left(\sum_{i=1}^{n} e_i^2 \right) = -2 \sum_{i=1}^{n} x_i^k (y_i - b_0 - b_1 x_i - b_2 x_i^2 - \ldots$$
$$- b_k x_i^k - \ldots - b_p x_i^p) = 0$$

thus

$$b_0 \sum_{i=1}^{n} x_i^k + b_1 \sum_{i=1}^{n} x_i x_i^k + b_2 \sum_{i=1}^{n} x_i^2 x_i^k + \ldots + b_k \sum_{i=1}^{n} (x_i^k)^2 + \ldots$$
$$+ b_p \sum_{i=1}^{n} x_i^p x_i^k = \sum_{i=1}^{n} y_i x_i^k$$

Using Eq. (4.15) to eliminate b_0, we get

$$b_1 \sum_{i=1}^{n} x_i^k (x_i - \bar{x}) + b_2 \sum_{i=1}^{n} x_i^k (x_i^2 - \overline{x^2}) + \ldots + b_k \sum_{i=1}^{n} x_i^k (x_i^k - \overline{x^k})$$
$$+ b_p \sum_{i=1}^{n} x_i^k (x_i^p - \overline{x^p}) = \sum_{i=1}^{n} x_i^k (y_i - \bar{y})$$

and hence, since

$$\sum_{i=1}^{n} x_i^k (x_i - \bar{x}) = \sum_{i=1}^{n} (x_i^k - \overline{x^k})(x_i - \bar{x}), \text{ etc.:}$$

$$b_1 \sum_{i=1}^{n} (x_i - \bar{x})(x_i^k - \overline{x^k}) + b_2 \sum_{i=1}^{n} (x_i^2 - \overline{x_i^2})(x^k - \overline{x^k}) + b_k \sum_{i=1}^{n} (x_i^k - \overline{x^k})^2$$

$$+ \ldots + b_p \sum_{i=1}^{n} (x_i^p + \overline{x^p})(x_i^k - \overline{x^k})$$

$$= \sum_{i=1}^{n} (y_i - \bar{y})(x_i^k - \overline{x^k}) \quad (4.16)$$

Equation (4.16) can be rewritten in condensed notation as

$$b_1 C_{1k} + b_2 C_{2k} + b_k C_{kk} + \ldots + b_p C_{pk} = C_{yk} \quad (4.17)$$

where the "C" notations indicate the respective summed products. For example,

$$C_{1k} = \sum_{i=1}^{n} (x_i - \bar{x})(x_i^k - \overline{x^k})$$

where the subscript $1k$ refers to the exponents of x. Note that y is used direct as a subscript.

Equation (4.17) represents a set of p simultaneous equations for the curvilinear regression coefficients $b_1, b_2, \ldots b_p$. Written in more detail, these take the general form:

$$\left.\begin{aligned}
b_1 C_{11} + b_2 C_{21} + b_3 C_{31} + \ldots + b_p C_{p1} &= C_{y1} \\
b_1 C_{12} + b_2 C_{22} + b_3 C_{32} + \ldots + b_p C_{p2} &= C_{y2} \\
b_1 C_{13} + b_2 C_{23} + b_3 C_{33} + \ldots + b_p C_{p3} &= C_{y3} \\
\vdots \qquad \vdots \qquad \vdots \qquad\qquad \vdots \qquad &\vdots \\
b_1 C_{1p} + b_2 C_{2p} + b_3 C_{3p} + \ldots + b_p C_{pp} &= C_{yp}
\end{aligned}\right\} \quad (4.18)$$

Equations (4.18) and (4.15) give the least squares estimates of a curvilinear regression of y on the successive powers of x, namely; $x^1, x^2, x^3, \ldots, x^p$.

It is valuable to note that the linear regression is a special case of curvilinear regression with $p = 1$. The original value for b_0 in a linear equation is therefore derived from Eq. (4.15) as $b_0 = \bar{y} - b_1\bar{x}$, the same as Eq. (4.6); and from Eq. (4.18)

$$b_1 \sum_{i=1}^{n} (x_i - \bar{x})^2 = \sum_{i=1}^{n} (y_i - \bar{y})(x_i - \bar{x})$$

$$\therefore b_1 = \sum_{i=1}^{n} (y_i - \bar{y})(x_i - \bar{x}) \bigg/ \sum_{i=1}^{n} (x_i - \bar{x})^2$$

which is analogous to Eq. (4.7) in different form.

It becomes obvious that when p increases, the complexity of calculation increases quite rapidly. We will therefore limit our manual solutions to second-order examples. The solution of higher-order problems should utilize the services of a computer or certain shortcut numerical analysis methods should be used. Such methods are outside the scope of this book.

4.1.8 Example. Determine the parabolic regression of tensile strength on hardness in Example 4.1.3.

Solution: A parabolic regression is a second-order equation

$$y' = b_0 + b_1 x + b_2 x^2$$

for $p = 2$. Thus, Eq. (4.18) becomes

$$b_1 C_{11} + b_2 C_{21} = C_{y1}$$
$$b_1 C_{12} + b_2 C_{22} = C_{y2}$$

and Eq. (4.15) becomes

$$b_0 = \bar{y} - b_1 \bar{x} - b_2 \overline{x^2}$$

In alternate forms, the above C notations are

$$C_{y1} = \sum (y - \bar{y})(x - \bar{x}) = \sum xy - \frac{(\sum x)(\sum y)}{n}$$

$$C_{11} = \sum (x - \bar{x})^2 = \sum x^2 - \frac{(\sum x)^2}{n}$$

$$C_{21} = \sum (x^2 - \overline{x^2})(x - \bar{x}) = \sum x^3 - \frac{(\sum x^2)(\sum x)}{n}$$

$$C_{12} = C_{21}$$

$$C_{22} = \sum (x^2 - \overline{x^2})^2 = \sum x^4 - \frac{(\sum x^2)^2}{n}$$

$$C_{y2} = \sum (y - \bar{y})(x^2 - \overline{x^2}) = \sum x^2 y - \frac{(\sum y)(\sum x^2)}{n}$$

We know from Example 4.1.3, that

$$\sum x = 42.1; \quad \sum y = 46,200; \quad \sum x^2 = 200.49$$

and $$\sum xy = 233,180.0$$

We must compute $\sum x^3$, $\sum x^2 y$, $\sum x^4$, thus:

	x^3	$x^2 y$	x^4
1	68.88	68,921.00	282.58
2	91.12	93,150.00	410.06
3	2.74	392.00	3.84
4	9.24	3,969.00	19.45
5	27.00	18,900.00	81.00
6	205.38	264,556.00	1,211.74
7	140.61	175,760.00	731.16
8	74.09	104,076.00	311.17
9	226.98	275,354.00	1,384.58
10	175.62	216,384.00	983.45
$\sum$	1,021.66	1,221,462.00	5,419.03

$$\bar{y} = \frac{46,200}{10} = 4,620$$

$$\bar{x} = \frac{42.1}{10} = 4.21$$

$$\overline{x^2} = \frac{200.49}{10} = 20.05$$

Solving,

$$C_{11} = \sum x^2 - \frac{(\sum x)^2}{n} = 200.49 - \frac{(42.1)^2}{10} = 23.25$$

$$C_{21} = \sum x^3 - \frac{(\sum x^2)(\sum x)}{n} = 1,021.66 - \frac{(200.49)(42.1)}{10} = 177.60$$

$$C_{y1} = \sum xy - \frac{(\sum x)(\sum y)}{n} = 233,180.0 - \frac{(42.1)(46,200)}{10} = 38,678$$

$$C_{22} = \sum x^4 - \frac{(\sum x^2)^2}{n} = 5,419.03 - \frac{(200.49)^2}{10} = 1,399.41$$

$$C_{y2} = \sum x^2 y - \frac{(\sum x^2)(\sum y)}{n} = 1,221,462.0 - \frac{(200.49)(46,200)}{10}$$

$$= 293,846$$

Substituting in original equations,

$$23.25b_1 +\ \ \ 177.60b_2 =\ \ \ 38,678$$
$$177.60b_1 + 1,399.41b_2 = 293,846$$

Solving for b_1 in first equation,

$$b_1 = \frac{38,678 - 177.60b_2}{23.25}$$

$$= 1,620.56 - 7.6387b_2$$

and substituting in second equation,

$$1,399.41b_2 = 293,846 - 177.60(1,620.56 - 7.6387b_2)$$

$$b_2 = \frac{293,846 - 287,811,456}{42.78} = 141.06$$

Substituting b_2 into first equation,

$$b_1 = \frac{38,678 - 177.60\,(141.06)}{23.25}$$

$$= 543.04$$

Substituting in third equation,

$$b_0 = \bar{y} - b_1\bar{x} - b_2\overline{x^2}$$
$$= 4{,}620 - 543.04\,(4.21) - 141.06\,(20.05)$$
$$= 4{,}077.45$$

giving the regression equation

$$y' = 4{,}077.45 + 543.04x + 141.06x^2 \quad \text{(coded)}$$

4.2   Levels of Variable Predetermined

So far in this chapter we have dealt with the analysis of experiment with a single independent variable whose levels have not been predetermined. We will now be concerned with such experiments when the level of the independent variable have been predetermined. As previously mentioned, this preset condition can result from two basic circumstances (1) The variable can be qualitative and therefore discrete levels are implied or (2) the variable is quantitative and the levels are present for convenience or as a necessity.

We will first illustrate this situation with a logic diagram:

Theoretical Distribution	$-f(x)\rightarrow$	jth Level of Variable (x)	$-x_j\rightarrow$	The Experiment	$-y_{ij}\rightarrow$

This diagram illustrates the content of a final response, y_{ij}. Such a response is drawn from an x_j level of the variable x whose frequency function is $f(x)$ Within the experiment, the response y_{ij} can be explained as a quantity that contains the following effects:

$$y_{ij} = \mu + \tau_j + \varepsilon_{ij} \tag{4.19}$$

where y_{ij} is the ith response $(i = 1, 2, \ldots n_j)$ on the jth level of the independent variable with $j = 1, 2, \ldots k$. The μ is the grand mean of the experiment and is a fixed effect. τ_j represents the effect of the jth level of the random variable x. The ε_{ij} is the random error in the ith trial of the jth level, whose mean is zero and variance is constant for all levels.

For our purposes here it is assumed that the τ_j's are normally and independently distributed with

$$\sum_{j=1}^{k} \tau_j = 0$$

A general form layout of an experiment of this type is shown in Table 4.7.

4.2.1 Estimate of Experimental Variance. As in Sec. 4.1.4 we will now estimate the variances in such an experiment. This will first be done in

TABLE 4.7

General Experimental Layout

Levels	Independent Variable (x)			
	x_1	x_2 . . . . . x_j . . . . . x_k		
Responses	y_{11} y_{21} y_{i1} . . . . . $y_{n_1 1}$	y_{12} . . . . . y_{1j} . . . . . y_{1k} y_{22} . . . . . y_{2j} . . . . . y_{2k} y_{i2} . . . . . y_{ij} . . . . . y_{ik} . . . . $y_{n_{ij}}$ . . . $y_{n_2 2}$ $y_{n_k k}$		
Totals	$y_{.1}$	$y_{.2}$	$y_{.j}$	$y_{.k}$ $y_{..}$
Number	n_1	n_2	n_j	n_k N
Means	$\bar{y}_{.1}$	$\bar{y}_{.2}$	$\bar{y}_{.j}$	$\bar{y}_{.k}$ $\bar{y}_{..}$

Sec. 4.2.2 using the regression principle. The analysis of variance method will then be presented in Sec. 4.2.4 as a more useful method of performing the operations that are required in estimating the variances.

4.2.2 The Regression Method. Equation (4.19) may be rewritten

$$y_{ij} = \bar{y} + t_j + e_{ij} \qquad (4.20)$$

where $\bar{y}$ is a best estimate of μ, t_j's are best estimates of the τ_j's, and e_{ij} is a best estimate of ε_{ij}. Since the levels of the variable x are set up in columns in Table 4.7, it is traditional to refer to them as *column effects*.

Our purpose is to determine these best estimates [18]. We first form the sum of squares of the errors by rewriting Eq. (4.20) and squaring each side

$$\sum_{i=1}^{n} \sum_{j=1}^{k} e_{ij}^2 = \sum_{i=1}^{n} \sum_{j=1}^{k} (y_{ij} - \bar{y} - t_j)^2 \qquad (4.21)$$

with the double summation referring to the ith response of the jth columns.

We wish to determine the estimates of $\bar{y}$ and t_j that will minimize the sum of squares of these errors. We, therefore, differentiate with respect to $\bar{y}, t_1, t_2, \ldots t_k$ when $j = 1, 2, \ldots k$.

Thus

$$\frac{\partial}{\partial \bar{y}} \left(\sum_{i=1}^{n} \sum_{j=1}^{k} e_{ij}^2 \right) = -2 \sum_{i=1}^{n} \sum_{j=1}^{k} (y_{ij} - \bar{y} - t_j) = 0$$

$$\frac{\partial}{\partial t_1} \left(\sum_{i=1}^{n_1} e_{i1}^2 \right) = -2 \sum_{i=1}^{n_1} (y_{i1} - \bar{y} - t_1) = 0$$

$$\frac{\partial}{\partial t_2} \left(\sum_{i=1}^{n_2} e_{i2}^2 \right) = -2 \sum_{i=1}^{n_2} (y_{i2} - \bar{y} - t_2) = 0$$

$$\frac{\partial}{\partial t_k} \left(\sum_{i=1}^{n_j} e_{ij}^2 \right) = -2 \sum_{i=1}^{n_j} (y_{ik} - \bar{y} - t_k) = 0$$

These give the following least squares normal equations:

$$\sum_{i=1}^{n} \sum_{j=1}^{k} y_{ij} = \sum_{i=1}^{n_j} \sum_{j=1}^{k} \bar{y} + \sum_{i=1}^{n_j} \sum_{j=1}^{k} t_j$$

$$\sum_{i=1}^{n_1} y_{i1} = \sum_{i=1}^{n_1} \bar{y} + \sum_{i=1}^{n_1} t_1$$

$$\sum_{i=1}^{n_2} y_{i2} = \sum_{i=1}^{n_2} \bar{y} + \sum_{i=1}^{n_2} t_2$$

$$\sum_{i=1}^{n_j} y_{ik} = \sum_{i=1}^{n_j} \bar{y} + \sum_{i=1}^{n_j} t_k$$

Substituting the general experimental notation that is used in Table 4.7, where

$$y_{..} = \sum_{i=1}^{n} \sum_{j=1}^{k} y_{ij} \qquad y_{.k} = \sum_{i=1}^{n_j} y_{ik}$$

$$N\bar{y} = \sum_{i=1}^{n} \sum_{j=1}^{k} \bar{y} \qquad n_j \bar{y} = \sum_{i=1}^{n_j} y$$

$$n_j \sum_{j=1}^{k} t_j = \sum_{i=1}^{n_j} \sum_{j=1}^{k} t_j \qquad n_j t_k = \sum_{i=1}^{n_j} t_k$$

we rewrite the least squares normal equations

$$\left. \begin{array}{l} y_{..} = N\bar{y} + n_j \sum_{j=1}^{k} t_j \\[2mm] y_{.1} = n_1 \bar{y} + n_1 t_1 \\ y_{.2} = n_2 \bar{y} + n_2 t_2 \\ \quad \cdot \qquad \cdot \\ \quad \cdot \qquad \cdot \\ \quad \cdot \qquad \cdot \\ y_{.k} = n_j \bar{y} + n_j t_k \end{array} \right\} \qquad \textbf{(4.22)}$$

Knowing that since t_j is an estimate of τ_j, then

$$\sum_{j=1}^{k} t_j = 0$$

Therefore, from Eq. (4.22)

$$\bar{y} = \frac{y_{..}}{N} = \bar{y}_{..}$$

$$t_1 = \frac{y_{.1} - n_1\bar{y}}{n_1} = \frac{y_{.1}}{n_1} - \frac{y_{..}}{N} = \bar{y}_{.1} - \bar{y}_{..} \tag{4.23}$$

$$t_2 = \frac{y_{.2} - n_2\bar{y}}{n_2} = \frac{y_{.2}}{n_2} - \frac{y_{..}}{N} = \bar{y}_{.2} - \bar{y}_{..}$$

$$t_k = \frac{y_{.k} - n_k\bar{y}}{n_k} = \frac{y_{.k}}{n_k} - \frac{y_{..}}{N} = \bar{y}_{.k} - \bar{y}_{..}$$

giving a general form solution for each best estimate.

To obtain an estimate of the error sum of squares in the above terms, we first rewrite Eq. (4.21) thus,

$$\sum_{j=1}^{k} \sum_{i=1}^{n} e_{ij}^2 = \text{S.S.}_{\text{error}} = \sum_{j=1}^{k} \sum_{i=1}^{n} (y_{ij} - [\bar{y} + t_j])^2$$

and substitute the best estimates from Eq. (4.23) and expand the square so that

$$\text{S.S.}_{\text{error}} = \sum_{i=1}^{n_j} \sum_{j=1}^{k} y_{ij}^2 - 2 \sum_{i=1}^{n_j} \sum_{j=1}^{k} y_{ij}(\bar{y} - t_j) + \sum_{i=1}^{n_j} \sum_{j=1}^{k} (\bar{y} + t_j)^2$$

$$= \sum_{i=1}^{n_j} \sum_{j=1}^{k} y_{ij}^2 - 2\bar{y} \sum_{i=1}^{n} \sum_{j=1}^{k} y_{ij} - 2 \sum_{i=1}^{n_j} \sum_{j=1}^{k} y_{ij}t_j$$

$$+ \bar{y}^2 N + 2\bar{y} \sum_{i=1}^{n} \sum_{j=1}^{k} t_j + \sum_{i=1}^{n_j} \sum_{j=1}^{k} t_j^2$$

$$\text{S.S.}_{\text{error}} = \sum_{i=1}^{n_j} \sum_{j=1}^{k} y_{ij}^2 - 2\bar{y} \sum_{i=1}^{n} \sum_{j=1}^{k} y_{ij} - 2 \sum_{i=1}^{n_j} \sum_{j=1}^{k} y_{ij}t_j$$

$$+ \bar{y}(N\bar{y} + n \sum_{j=1}^{k} t_j) + \sum_{j=1}^{k} t_j(n\bar{y} + nt_j)$$

From Eq. (4.22) we substitute

$$\text{S.S.}_{\text{error}} = \sum_{i=1}^{n_j} \sum_{j=1}^{k} y_{ij}^2 - 2\bar{y}y_{..} - 2 \sum_{i=1}^{n_j} \sum_{j=1}^{k} y_{ij}t_j + \bar{y}y_{..} + \sum_{j=1}^{k} y_{.j}t_j$$

$$= \sum_{i=1}^{n_j} \sum_{j=1}^{k} y_{ij}^2 - \bar{y}y_{..} - \sum_{j=1}^{k} y_{.j}t_j$$

$$= \sum_{i=1}^{n_j} \sum_{j=1}^{k} (y_{ij} - \bar{y}_{..})^2 - \sum_{j=1}^{k} y_{.j}t_j \tag{4.24}$$

which can be read as the difference between the total sum of squares and
the regression sum of squares. Therefore, from (4.24)

$$\text{S.S.}_{\text{regression}} = \sum_{i=1}^{n_j} \sum_{j=1}^{k} (y_{ij} - \bar{y}_{..})^2 - \text{S.S.}_{\text{error}}$$

$$= \sum_{j=1}^{k} y_{.j} t_j$$

$$= \sum_{j=1}^{k} y_{.j}(\bar{y}_{.j} - \bar{y}_{..}) \tag{4.25}$$

It can be seen that $t_j = \sum (\bar{y}_{.j} - \bar{y})$ in experimental notation. We can
therefore summarize the above calculations in Table 4.8.

TABLE 4.8

General ANOVA Table

Source of Variation	S.S.	ν	M.S.
Due to Regression	$\sum_{j=1}^{k} \bar{y}_{.j} (y_{.j} - \bar{y}_{..})$	1	S.S./1
About Regression (Error)	$\sum_{i=1}^{n_j} \sum_{j=1}^{k} (y_{ij} - \bar{y}_{..})^2$ $- \sum_{j=1}^{k} y_{.j} (\bar{y}_{.j} - \bar{y}_{..})$	$N-2$	S.S./$(N-2)$
Total	$\sum_{i=1}^{n_j} \sum_{j=1}^{n} (y_{ij} - \bar{y}_{..})^2$	$N-1$	

Comparison of this table to Table 4.4, page 64, will reveal a similarity
in terms. Table 4.8 represents the regression analysis of Equation (4.20)

$$y_{ij} = \bar{y} + t_j + e_{ij}$$

where t_j is the estimate of true column effects, τ_j. If we should assume that
$\tau_j = 0$, that is, none of the variance of y can be explained by the variance
in x, we can rewrite Eq. (4.20) thus,

$$y_{ij} = \bar{y} + e_{ij} \tag{4.26}$$

If we calculate the regression sum of squares for Eq. (4.26) and subtract it from the regression sum of squares in Eq. (4.25), we will determine
the sum of squares for t_j, or the sum of squares due to column effects.
This will now be done.

Equation (4.26) can be rewritten

$$e_{ij} = y_{ij} - \bar{y}$$

and the least squares applied to the error as before

$$\sum_{i=1}^{n_i} \sum_{j=1}^{k} e_{ij} = \sum_{i=1}^{n_i} \sum_{j=1}^{k} (y_{ij} - \bar{y})^2$$

Similarly, Eq. (4.25) can be written

$$\text{S.S.}_{\text{regression}} = \bar{y}_{..} y_{..} \tag{4.27}$$

since the last term of Eq. (4.24) is zero because $\tau_j = 0$. We can therefore write

$$\text{S.S.}_{\text{columns}} = \text{S.S.}_{\text{regression } (\tau_j \neq 0)} - \text{S.S.}_{\text{regression } (\tau_j = 0)} \tag{4.28}$$

$$\therefore \text{S.S.}_{\text{columns}} = \bar{y}_{..} y_{..} + \sum_{j=1}^{k} y_{.j}(\bar{y}_{.j} - \bar{y}_{..}) - \bar{y}_{..} y_{..}$$

$$= \sum_{j=1}^{k} y_{.j} (\bar{y}_{.j} - \bar{y}_{..})$$

$$= \sum_{j=1}^{k} y_{.j} \left(\frac{y_{.j}}{n_j} - \frac{y_{..}}{N} \right)$$

$$= \sum_{j=1}^{k} \frac{y_{.j}^2}{n_j} - \frac{y_{..}}{N} \sum_{j=1}^{k} y_{.j}$$

$$\text{S.S.}_{\text{columns}} = \sum_{j=1}^{k} \frac{y_{.j}^2}{n_j} - \frac{y_{..}^2}{N} \quad \text{since} \quad \sum_{j=1}^{k} y_{.j} = y_{..} \tag{4.29}$$

As before, we know

$$\text{S.S.}_{\text{error}} = \text{S.S.}_{\text{total}} - \text{S.S.}_{\text{regression } (\tau_j \neq 0)} \tag{4.30}$$

$$= \sum_{i=1}^{n_i} \sum_{j=1}^{k} y_{ij}^2 - \frac{y_{..}^2}{N} - \sum_{j=1}^{k} y_{.j}(\bar{y}_{.j} - \bar{y}_{..})$$

$$= \sum_{i=1}^{n_i} \sum_{j=1}^{k} y_{ij}^2 - \frac{y_{..}^2}{N} - \sum_{j=1}^{k} \frac{y_{.j}^2}{n} + \frac{y_{..}^2}{N}$$

$$= \sum_{i=1}^{n_i} \sum_{j=1}^{k} y_{ij}^2 - \sum_{j=1}^{k} \frac{y_{.j}^2}{n} \tag{4.31}$$

and is summarized in Table 4.9.

TABLE 4.9

General ANOVA Table

Source of Variation	S.S.	ν	M.S.
Columns	$\sum_{j=1}^{k} \dfrac{y_{.j}^2}{n_j} - \dfrac{y_{..}^2}{N}$	$k-1$	S.S./$(k-1)$
Error	$\sum_{i=1}^{n_j} \sum_{j=1}^{n} y_{ij}^2 - \sum_{j=1}^{k} \dfrac{y_{.j}^2}{n_j}$	$N-k$	S.S./$(N-k)$
Total	$\sum_{i=1}^{n_j} \sum_{j=1}^{k} y_{ij}^2 - \dfrac{y_{..}^2}{N}$	$N-1$	

The summary in Table 4.9 represents the general analysis of the variances in an experiment with one dependent variable and where the levels of the variable have been predetermined. Interpretation of these results will be covered in Chapters 7 and 8.

4.2.3   Example. For the data in Table 4.10 make an analysis of the variances using the regression method.

TABLE 4.10

Data for Example 4.2.3

	Columns			
	1	2	3	4
	0	1	5	0
	3	2	5	1
	4	1	4	0
	1	4	2	3
	6	3	6	2
Total	14	11	22	6
Number	5	5	5	5
Mean	2.8	2.2	4.4	1.2

Solution: (a) Sum each column:

$$y_{.1} = 14$$
$$y_{.2} = 11$$
$$y_{.3} = 22$$
$$y_{.4} = 6$$

(b) Calculate $\bar{y}$:

$$\bar{y} = \bar{y}_{..} = \frac{y_{.1} + y_{.2} + y_{.3} + y_{.4}}{N} = \frac{14 + 11 + 22 + 6}{20} = 2.65$$

(c) Calculate the column effects from Eq. (4.23):

$$t_1 = \bar{y}_{.1} - \bar{y}_{..} = \tfrac{14}{5} - \tfrac{53}{20} = .15$$
$$t_2 = \tfrac{11}{5} - 2.65 = -.45$$
$$t_3 = \tfrac{22}{5} - 2.65 = 1.75$$
$$t_4 = \tfrac{6}{5} - 2.65 = -1.45$$

(d) Calculate regression sum of squares from Eq. (4.25):

$$\begin{aligned}
\text{S.S.}_{\text{regression } (\tau_j \neq 0)} &= 2.65(53) + 14(0.15) + 11(-0.45) + 22(1.75) \\
&\quad + 6(-1.45) \\
&= 167.40
\end{aligned}$$

and from Eq. (4.27):

$$\text{S.S.}_{\text{regression } (\tau_j = 0)} = \bar{y}_{..}\, y_{..} = 2.65(53) = 140.45$$

From Eq. (4.28):

$$\text{S.S.}_{\text{columns}} = 167.40 - 140.45 = 26.95$$

From Eq. (4.30):

$$\begin{aligned}
\text{S.S.}_{\text{error}} &= \sum y^2 - \text{S.S.}_{\text{regression } (\tau_j \neq 0)} \\
&= (0)^2 + (3)^2 + (4)^2 + \ldots + (2)^2 - 167.40 \\
&= 213 - 167.40 = 45.60
\end{aligned}$$

TABLE 4.11
ANOVA Table for Example 4.2.3

Source of Variation	S.S.	ν	M.S.
Columns	26.95	3	8.98
Error	45.60	16	2.77
Total	72.55	19	

4.2.4   The Analysis of Variance Method. A more direct method of calculation can be made using the developed Equations (4.29) and (4.30). The Example 4.2.3 will be used to illustrate this method:

(a) Calculate total sum of squares:

$$\text{S.S.}_{\text{total}} = \sum y^2 - \frac{(\sum y)^2}{N} = 213 - \frac{(53)^2}{20} = 72.55$$

(b) Calculate column sum of squares:

$$\text{S.S.}_{\text{columns}} = \sum_{j=1}^{4} \frac{\sum y_j^2}{n} - \frac{(\sum y)^2}{N}$$

$$= \frac{(14)^2}{5} + \frac{(11)^2}{5} + \frac{(22)^2}{5} + \frac{(6)^2}{5} - \frac{(53)^2}{20}$$

$$= 26.95$$

(c) Calculate sum of squares for error:

$$\text{S.S.}_{\text{error}} = \text{S.S.}_{\text{total}} - \text{S.S.}_{\text{columns}} = 72.55 - 26.95$$
$$= 45.60$$

These are the same values as in Table 4.11.

4.2.5 Example. An open circuit test on four different 50-KVA 2,400/240 volt transformers was made under similar operating conditions. The power output was measured for each at one-hour intervals, producing the following results:

TABLE 4.12

Power Output in Watts for Four 50-KVA 2400/240 Volt Transformers

	Transformer		
A	B	C	D
186	187	170	186
180	182	180	184
192	183	180	184
181	178	182	183
179	185	183	185

Make an analysis of variance for this test and construct an ANOVA table.

Solution: Calculate sums and squares from data in Table 4.1.2:

	A	A^2	B	B^2	C	C^2	D	D^2
1	186	34,596	187	34,969	179	32,041	186	34,596
2	180	32,400	182	33,124	180	32,400	184	33,856
3	192	36,864	183	33,489	180	32,400	184	33,856
4	181	32,761	178	31,684	182	33,124	183	33,489
5	179	32,041	185	34,225	183	33,489	185	34,225
	918	168,662	915	167,491	904	163,454	922	170,022

Grand Total = 3,659
Calculate the sum of squares terms:

$$\text{S.S.}_{\text{total}} = \sum y^2 - \frac{(\sum y)^2}{N} = (186)^2 + (180)^2 + \ldots$$

$$+ (183)^2 + (185)^2 - \frac{(3659)^2}{20}$$

$$= 669,629 - 669,414 = 215$$

$$\text{S.S.}_{\text{columns}} = \frac{\sum y_j^2}{n_j} - \frac{y^2}{N} = \frac{(918)^2}{5} + \frac{(915)^2}{5} + \frac{(904)^2}{5} + \frac{(922)^2}{5}$$

$$- \frac{(3659)^2}{20}$$

$$= 168,544.8 + 167,445.0 + 163,443.2 + 170,016.8$$
$$- 669,414.0$$

$$= 35.8$$

$$\text{S.S.}_{\text{error}} = \text{S.S.}_{\text{total}} - \text{S.S.}_{\text{column.}}$$

$$= 215 - 35.8 = 179.2$$

Construct ANOVA as follows:

Source of Variation	S.S.	ν	M.S.
Columns	35.8	3	11.9
Error	179.2	16	11.2
Total	215.0	19	

Degrees of freedom are calculated:
Total degrees of freedom $= N - 1 = 20 - 1 = 19$
Column degrees of freedom $= k - 1 = 4 - 1 = 3$
Error degrees of freedom $= (N - 1) - (k - 1) = 19 - 3 = 16$

4.3 Exercises (Data sets are in Appendix D.)

4.1. Consider data set 2. Plot the scatter diagram of (a) y versus x_1, (b) y versus x_2, (c) y versus x_3.

4.2. Consider data set 2. Compute the regression of (a) y on x_1, (b) y on x_2, (c) y on x_3.

4.3. Plot the linear regression equations computed in Exercise 4.2 on the respective scatter diagrams of Exercise 4.1.

4.4. Given the linear regression equations of Exercise 4.2, compute the value of y when (a) $x_1 = 20$, (b) $x_2 = 7$, (c) $x_3 = 350$.

4.5. Calculate the sum of squares for regression, and construct an ANOVA table for: (a) y as a function of x_1, (b) y as a function of x_2, (c) y as a function of x_3.

4.6. Determine the parabolic regression of y on x_1 from data set 2.

4.7. Given data set 4, it is desirable to know whether plastic RL-2405 foam is consistent with respect to the four positions, A, B, C, and D. Therefore, conduct an analysis of variance on the data set. Write the mathematical model and construct the ANOVA table.

4.8. Conduct an analysis of variance on data set 4 where layers are considered the variable. Write the mathematical model and construct the ANOVA table.

4.9. Assume in data set 2 that x_1 is the dependent variable and y is the independent variable. (a) Compute the regression of x_1 on y. (b) Compare your results with those in Exercise 4.2 (a).

CHAPTER 5

Analysis of Experiments
with Multiple Independent Variables

Chapter 4 was limited to the analysis of data drawn from experiments with only one independent variable identified. We will now expand these concepts into situations that involve *more than one* independent variable. As before, such experiments can be designed with the levels of each variable not predetermined, producing a similar type of situation to that in Sec. 4.1. In other experimental situations the variables may have predetermined levels so that a multidimensional matrix is involved. This chapter will be concerned essentially with the analysis of the variances in such multidimensional experiments.

5.1 Level of Variables Not Predetermined

The case of an experiment with multiple independent variables identified can be illustrated as follows:

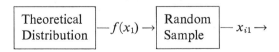

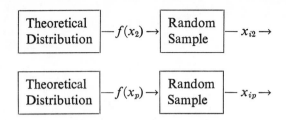

where $f(x_1), f(x_2), \ldots f(x_p)$ represents the frequency functions for the independent variables $x_1, x_2, \ldots x_p$. The outputs from the random samples, $x_{i1}, x_{i2}, \ldots x_{ip}$, represent the ith trial from the pth variable, x_p.

For the experiment the random samples of the independent variables become inputs and the response, y_i, of the dependent variable becomes the output to the experiment, thus:

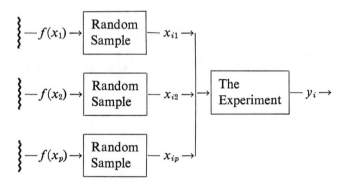

where y_i represents the ith response of the dependent variable, y.

For the case when the levels of a variable are not predetermined, the input-output data would be as shown in Table 5.1 where x_{ik} is the ith response of the kth independent variable, x_k, when $i = 1, 2, \ldots, n$ and $k = 1, 2, \ldots, p$.

5.1.1 Multiple Linear Regression. In Chapter 4 the discussion was limited to the regression of a dependent variable on a single independent variable. A linear regression of the variable y_1 upon the variables $x_1, x_2, \ldots x_p$ may be written

$$y_i = \beta_0 + \beta_1 x_{i1} + \beta_2 x_{i2} + \ldots + \beta_k x_{ik} + \varepsilon_{ik} \tag{5.1}$$

and the regression estimate, y_i', would be determined by

$$y_i' = b_0 + b_1 x_{i1} + b_2 x_{i2} + \ldots + b_k x_{ik} \tag{5.2}$$

where y_i' is the regression estimate of y_i, and $b_0, b_1, b_2, \ldots, b_k$ are best esti-

TABLE 5.1

Input-Output Data for Multidimensional Experiment

Response Number	Independent Variables					Dependent Variable
	x_1	x_2	x_k	x_p		y
1	x_{11}	x_{12}	x_{1k}	x_{1p}		y_1
2	x_{21}	x_{22}	x_{2k}	x_{2p}		y_2
.	.	.	.	.		.
.	.	.	.	.		.
.	.	.	.	.		.
.	.	.	.	.		.
.	.	.	.	.		.
i	x_{i1}	x_{i2}	x_{ik}	x_{ip}		y_i
.	.	.	.	.		.
.	.	.	.	.		.
.	.	.	.	.		.
.	.	.	.	.		.
n	x_{n1}	x_{n2}	x_{nk}	x_{np}		y_n

mates of $\beta_0, \beta_1, \beta_2, \ldots, \beta_k$. The error in estimating the true value of y_i by the regression estimate y_i' is

$$e_{ik} = y_i - (b_0 + b_1 x_{i1} + b_2 x_{i2} + \ldots + b_k x_{ik}) \qquad (5.3)$$

and from Eq. (5.2)

$$e_{ik} = y_i - y_i'$$

where e_{ik} is the error of estimation. This error in the ith response of the pth independent variable is therefore equal to the difference between the true response y_i and the regression estimate y_i'.

The values of the constants $b_0, b_1, b_2 \ldots b_k$ are unknown. As before, our problem is to derive those values for the constants which will give the best estimate of e_{ik}. This will be done by the method of least squares. Thus, we square both sides of Eq. (5.3) and sum the terms

$$\sum_{i=1}^{n} (e_{ik})^2 = \sum_{i=1}^{n} [y_i - (b_0 + b_1 x_{i1} + b_2 x_{i2} + \ldots + b_k x_{ik})]^2 \qquad (5.4)$$

We determine values for $b_0, b_1, b_2, \ldots b_k$ so as to minimize Eq. (5.4). The partial derivatives of Eq. (5.4) with respect to $b_0, b_1, b_2, \ldots b_k$ are each equated to zero, giving a set of simultaneous equations for the desired values of $b_0, b_1, b_2, \ldots b_k$.

Differentiating with respect to b_0 and equating to zero, we get

$$\partial/\partial b_0 \left(\sum_{i=1}^{n} e_{ik}^2 \right) = -2 \sum_{i=1}^{n} (y_i - b_0 - b_1 x_{i1} - \ldots - b_p x_{ip}) = 0$$

thus

$$n b_0 = \sum_{i=1}^{n} y_i - b_1 \sum_{i=1}^{n} x_{i1} - \ldots - b_p \sum_{i=1}^{n} x_{ip}$$

or

$$b_0 = \bar{y} - b_1 \bar{x}_1 - \ldots - b_p \bar{x}_p \tag{5.5}$$

For $k \neq 0$

$$\frac{\partial}{\partial b_k} \left(\sum_{i=1}^{n} e_i^2 \right)$$

$$= -2 \sum_{i=1}^{n} x_k (y - b_0 - b_1 x_{i1} - \ldots - b_k x_{ik} - \ldots - b_p x_{ip}) = 0$$

i.e.,

$$b_0 \sum_{i=1}^{n} x_{ik} + b_1 \sum_{i=1}^{n} x_{i1} x_{ik} + \ldots + b_k \sum_{i=1}^{n} x_{ik}^2 + \ldots + b_p \sum_{i=1}^{n} x_{ip} x_{ik}$$

$$= \sum_{i=1}^{n} y_i x_i \tag{5.6}$$

Substituting Eq. (5.5) in Eq. (5.6), we get

$$b_1 \sum_{i=1}^{n} x_{ik}(x_{i1} - \bar{x}_1) + \ldots + b_k \sum_{i=1}^{n} (x_{ik} - \bar{x}_k) + \ldots$$

$$+ b_p \sum_{i=1}^{n} x_{ik}(x_{ip} - \bar{x}_p) = \sum_{i=1}^{n} x_{ik}(y_i - \bar{y})$$

and since

$$\sum_{i=1}^{n} x_{ik}(x_{i1} - \bar{x}_1) = \sum (x_{ik} - \bar{x}_k)(x_{i1} - \bar{x}_1), \text{ etc.,}$$

$$b_1 \sum_{i=1}^{n} (x_{i1} - \bar{x}_1)(x_{ik} - \bar{x}_k) + \ldots + b_k \sum_{i=1}^{n} (x_{ik} - \bar{x}_k)^2 + \ldots$$

$$\ldots + b_p \sum_{i=1}^{n} (x_{ip} - \bar{x}_p)(x_{ik} - \bar{x}_k) = \sum_{i=1}^{n} (y_i - \bar{y})(x_{ik} - \bar{x}_k) \tag{5.7}$$

with $k = 1, 2, \ldots, p$.

Equation (5.7) can be written in the shorthand form

$$b_1 C_{1k} + \ldots + b_k C_{kk} + \ldots + b_p C_{pk} = C_{yk} \tag{5.8}$$

where C_{1k} denotes

$$\sum_{i=1}^{n} (x_{i1} - \bar{x}_1)(x_{ik} - \bar{x}_k)$$

with the subscripts $1, 2, 3, \ldots, k$ referring to the number of the independent variables and the subscript y denoting the dependent variable.

Equation (5.8) is identical to Eq. (4.17) in Chapter 4 except that the $k = 1, 2, \ldots p$ notation in Eq. (5.8) refers to the kth independent variable in a multiple linear regression while in Eq. (4.17), Chapter 4, the notation refers to the kth order of power in a curvilinear regression. In Eq. (5.8) we therefore have a set of p simultaneous equations for the multiple linear regression coefficients $b_1, b_2, \ldots, b_p$. Written in more detail, these take the general form:

$$\left.\begin{array}{l} b_1 C_{11} + b_2 C_{21} + b_3 C_{31} + \ldots + b_p C_{p1} = C_{y1} \\ b_1 C_{12} + b_2 C_{22} + b_3 C_{32} + \ldots + b_p C_{p2} = C_{y2} \\ b_1 C_{13} + b_2 C_{23} + b_3 C_{33} + \ldots + b_p C_{p3} = C_{y3} \\ \quad \cdot \qquad\quad \cdot \qquad\quad \cdot \qquad\qquad\quad \cdot \qquad\quad \cdot \\ \quad \cdot \qquad\quad \cdot \qquad\quad \cdot \qquad\qquad\quad \cdot \qquad\quad \cdot \\ \quad \cdot \qquad\quad \cdot \qquad\quad \cdot \qquad\qquad\quad \cdot \qquad\quad \cdot \\ b_1 C_{1p} + b_2 C_{2p} + b_3 C_{3p} + \ldots + b_p C_{pp} = C_{yp} \end{array}\right\} \qquad \textbf{(5.9)}$$

Equations (5.9) and (5.5) give the least squares estimates of the constants in the regression equation representing the dependence of y on $x_1, x_2, \ldots x_p$. For regression on only one variable ($p = 1$), Eqs. (5.9) and (5.5) reduce to Eqs. (4.7) and (4.6) in Chapter 4.

5.1.2   Example. An experiment was conducted to determine the relationship between temperature and vacuum, and the tensile strength of laminated plastic structural members. Plastic specimens were subjected to varying temperatures and vacuum pressures. The results of the experiment are shown in Table 5.2. Temperature was measured in degrees centigrade, and vacuum pressure in inches of mercury. Calculate the regression relationship between tensile strength and the two measured variables.

TABLE 5.2

Experimental Data for Example 5.1.2

Specimen No.	x_1 Temperature, °C	x_2 Pressure, in. Hg	y Tensile Strength, psi
1	−295	24.2	2,841
2	−275	27.6	3,421
3	−297	25.7	3,154
4	−273	27.7	2,850
5	−284	24.8	2,699
6	−283	24.1	3,417
7	−273	27.6	2,806
8	−280	24.6	2,413
9	−275	28.1	3,196
10	−285	24.1	3,005

Solution: The regression equation is written

$$y' = b_0 + b_1 x_1 + b_2 x_2$$

From Eq. (5.9), when $p = 2$

$$b_1 C_{11} + b_2 C_{21} = C_{y1}$$
$$b_1 C_{12} + b_2 C_{22} = C_{y2}$$

and from Eq. (5.5)

$$b_0 = \bar{y} - b_1 \bar{x}_1 - b_2 \bar{x}_2$$

giving three normal equations with three unknowns (b_0, b_1, and b_2). The C notations are

$$C_{11} = \sum (x_1 - \bar{x}_1)^2 = \sum x_1^2 - \frac{(\sum x_1)^2}{n}$$

$$C_{21} = \sum (x_2 - \bar{x}_2)(x_1 - \bar{x}_1) = \sum x_1 x_2 - \frac{(\sum x_1)(\sum x_2)}{n}$$

$$C_{y1} = \sum (y - \bar{y})(x_1 - \bar{x}_1) = \sum x_1 y - \frac{(\sum x_1)(\sum y)}{n}$$

$$C_{12} = C_{21}$$

$$C_{22} = \sum (x_2 - \bar{x}_2)^2 = \sum x_2^2 - \frac{(\sum x_2)^2}{n}$$

$$C_{y2} = \sum (y - \bar{y})(x_2 - \bar{x}_2) = \sum x_2 y - \frac{(\sum x_2)(\sum y)}{n}$$

Calculation of the terms needed in these equations is shown in Table 5.3. Substituting in the above equations we get

$$C_{11} = 795{,}912 - \frac{(-2820)^2}{10} = 390$$

$$C_{21} = -72{,}806.3 - \frac{(-2820)(258.5)}{10} = 90.72$$

$$C_{y1} = -8{,}394{,}726 - \frac{(29802)(-2820)}{10} = 9{,}438$$

$$C_{22} = 6{,}707.9 - \frac{(258.5)^2}{10} = 25.7$$

$$C_{y2} = 771{,}493.0 - \frac{(258.5)(29.802)}{10} = 1{,}111.3$$

and substituting in the normal equations

$$390 b_1 + 90.72 b_2 = 9{,}438$$
$$90.72 b_1 + 25.7 b_2 = 1{,}111.3$$
$$b_0 = 2{,}980.2 + 282 b_1 - 25.85 b_2$$

giving three equations with three unknowns. These unknowns can be determined by first solving for b_1 in the first equation thus

$$b_1 = \frac{9{,}438 - 90.72b_2}{390}$$

$$= 24.78 - .231b_2$$

We now substitute this value in the second equation and solve for b_2 thus

$$25.7b_2 = 1{,}111.3 - 90.72(24.78 - .231b_2)$$
$$b_2 = 186.411$$

Substituting this value back in the first equation gives

$$b_1 = \frac{9{,}438 - 90.72(186.411)}{390}$$

$$= 19.861$$

and substituting the values for b_1 and b_2 in the third equation gives

$$b_0 = 2{,}980.2 + 282(19.861) - 25.85(186.411)$$
$$= 3{,}762.278$$

The regression equation then becomes

$$y' = 3{,}762 + 19.861x_1 + 186.411x_2$$

5.1.3 Analysis of Multiple Linear Regression Variance. The analysis of the variances in multiple linear regression is similar to the case of a single independent variable with the sum of squares due to regression given by Eq. (4.12) in Chapter 4 as

$$\text{S.S.}_{\text{regression}} = b_1^2 \sum_{i=1}^{n} (x_i - \bar{x})^2 \tag{5.10}$$

and from Eq. (4.8) in Chapter 4,

$$b_1 = \sum_{i=1}^{n} (x_i -)\bar{x}(y_i - \bar{y}) \Big/ \sum_{i=1}^{n} (x_i - \bar{x})^2 \tag{5.11}$$

By combining Eqs. (5.10) and (5.11) above, we get

$$\text{S.S.}_{\text{regression}} = b_1 \sum_{i=1}^{n} (x_i - \bar{x})(y_i - \bar{y})$$

which is the sum of squares due to the regression of y upon a single independent variable x. Such can be written in shorthand notation as

$$\text{S.S.}_{\text{regression}} = b_1 C_{xy} \tag{5.12}$$

In notation for more than one independent variable the x subscript in

TABLE 5.3
Calculations for Example 5.1.2

	x_1	x_2	y	x_1^2	x_2^2	y^2	$x_1 x_2$	$x_1 y$	$x_2 y$
1	−295	24.2	2,841	87,025	585.6	8,071,281	−7,139.0	−838,095	68,752.2
2	−275	27.6	3,421	75,625	761.7	11,703,241	−7,590.0	−940,775	94,419.6
3	−297	25.7	3,154	88,209	660.4	9,947,716	−7,632.9	−927,276	81,057.8
4	−273	27.7	2,850	74,529	767.2	8,122,500	−7,562.1	−778,050	78,945.0
5	−284	24.8	2,699	80,656	615.0	7,284,601	−7,043.2	−766,516	66,935.2
6	−283	24.1	3,417	80,089	580.8	11,675,889	−6,820.3	−967,011	82,349.7
7	−273	27.6	2,806	74,529	761.7	7,873,636	−7,534.8	−766,038	77,445.6
8	−280	24.6	2,413	78,400	605.1	5,822,569	−6,888.0	−675,640	59,359.8
9	−275	28.1	3,196	75,625	789.6	10,214,416	−7,727.5	−878,900	89,807.6
10	−285	24.1	3,005	81,225	580.8	9,030,025	−6,868.5	−856,425	72,420.5
$\sum$	−2,820	258.5	29,802	795,912	6,707.9	89,745,874	−72,806.3	−8,394,726	771,493.0

$$\bar{x}_1 = \frac{-2,820}{10} = -282 \qquad \bar{x}_2 = \frac{258.5}{10} = 25.85 \qquad \bar{y} = \frac{29,802}{10} = 2,980.2$$

Eq. (5.12) would be designated by a 1, indicating the first variable of $x_1, x_2, \ldots x_p$ variables. Hence for p set of variables

$$\text{S.S.}_{\text{regression}} = b_1 C_{y1} + b_2 C_{y2} + \ldots + b_p C_{yp} \qquad (5.13)$$

with $b_1, b_2, \ldots b_p$ determined by the simultaneous solution of p equations. The total sum of squares is known to be

$$\text{S.S.}_{\text{total}} = \sum_{i=1}^{n} (y_i - \bar{y})^2 = C_{yy}$$

thus

$$\text{S.S.}_{\text{error}} = \text{S.S.}_{\text{total}} - \text{S.S.}_{\text{regression}} = C_{yy} - b_1 C_{y1} - \ldots - b_p C_{yp}$$

giving an estimate of the variance about regression.

The above can be summarized in Table 5.4.

TABLE 5.4

General ANOVA for Multiple Regression Variance

Source	S.S.	ν	M.S.
Due to Regression	$b_1 C_{y1} + b_2 C_{y2} + \ldots + b_p C_{yp}$	p	S.S./p
About Regression	$C_{yy} - b_1 C_{y1} - b_2 C_{y2} - \ldots - b_p C_{yp}$	$n - p - 1$	S.S./$(n - p - 1)$
Total	C_{yy}	$n - 1$	

5.1.4   Example. Referring to the data in Example 5.1.2, Table 5.2, compute the ANOVA table for regression variances.

Solution: From Table 5.4 we have for this problem ($p = 2$)

$$\text{S.S.}_{\text{due to regression}} = b_1 C_{y1} + b_2 C_{y2}$$
$$\text{S.S.}_{\text{about regression}} = C_{yy} - b_1 C_{y1} - b_2 C_{y2}$$

$$\text{S.S.}_{\text{total}} = C_{yy} = \sum y^2 - \frac{(\sum y)^2}{n}$$

From information in Example 5.1.2 we can calculate

$$\text{S.S.}_{\text{total}} = 99{,}693{,}590 - \frac{(29{,}802)^2}{10} = 10{,}877{,}669.6$$

$$\text{S.S.}_{\text{due to regression}} = (19.861)(9{,}438) + 186.411(1{,}111.3)$$
$$= 394{,}606.66$$

$$\text{S.S.}_{\text{about regression}} = 10{,}877{,}669.6 - 394{,}606.66 = 10{,}483{,}062.94$$

Giving the ANOVA table:

Source	S.S.	ν	M.S.
Due to Regression	394,606.66	2	197,303.33
About Regression	10,483,062.94	7	1,497,580.42
Total	10,877,669.6	9	

5.2 Levels of Variables Predetermined

As in Chapter 4 we have first considered in this chapter the experimental conditions where levels of the multiple independent variables have not been predetermined. We will now consider the condition when such variables are predetermined either by experimental choice or because of the variable's characteristics. This situation is illustrated as follows:

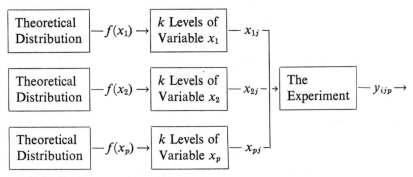

illustrating p number of independent variables arranged in k levels each.

Table 5.5 describes the content of a response y_{ijp} as being a result of the x_{cj} level of a variable x_c (for c number of p variables arranged in the columns of a matrix), combined with the x_{ri} level of a variable x_r (for r number of p variables arranged in the rows of a matrix). ($c + r = p$.) Such a response contains the following effects:

$$y_{ijp} = \mu + \tau_{cj} + \upsilon_{ri} + \varepsilon_{ij}$$

where μ is the common mean effect, τ_{cj} is the effect attributable to the cth variable in the jth column, υ_{ri} is the effect of the rth variable in the ith row, and ε_{ij} is the residual error.

It is assumed that the τ_{cj}'s and υ_{ri}'s are normally and independently distributed with

$$\sum_{j=1}^{k} \tau_{cj} = 0 \quad \text{and} \quad \sum_{i=1}^{\mu} \upsilon_{ri} = 0$$

For simplicity, Table 5.5 is limited to the cth independent variable (x_c) in the columns, and the rth independent variable (x_r) in the rows.

TABLE 5.5

General Experimental Data for Multiple Independent Variables

Row Variables		Column Variables (x_c)					Totals	Number	Means
		x_{c1}	x_{c2} ... x_{cj} ... x_{ck}						
	x_{r1}	y_{11p}	y_{12p} ... y_{1jp} ... y_{1kp}				$y_{1.p}$	k	$\bar{y}_{1.p}$
	x_{r2}	y_{21p}	y_{22p} ... y_{2jp} ... y_{2kp}				$y_{2.p}$	k	$\bar{y}_{2.p}$
	.	.	.	.	.		.	.	.
	.	.	.	.	.		.	.	.
x_r	.	.	.	.	.		.	.	.
	x_{ri}	y_{i1p}	y_{i2p} ... y_{ijp} ... y_{ikp}				$y_{i.p}$	k	$\bar{y}_{i.p}$
	.	.	.	.	.		.	.	.
	.	.	.	.	.		.	.	.
	.	.	.	.	.		.	.	.
	x_{rn}	y_{n1p}	y_{n2p} ... y_{njp} ... y_{nkp}				$y_{n.p}$	k	$\bar{y}_{n.p}$
Totals		$y_{.1p}$	$y_{.2p}$ ... $y_{.jp}$ ... $y_{.kp}$				$y_{..p}$		
Number		n	n ... n ... n					N	
Means		$\bar{y}_{.1p}$	$\bar{y}_{.2p}$ ... $\bar{y}_{.jp}$ ... $\bar{y}_{.kp}$						$\bar{y}_{..p}$

5.2.1   The Analysis of Variance Method. From Table 5.5 we can write

$$S.S._{total} = \sum_{j=1}^{k} \sum_{i=1}^{n} y_{ijp}^2 - \frac{y_{..p}^2}{N}$$

And as in Chapter 4 Eq. (4.29)

$$S.S._{columns} = \sum_{j=1}^{k} \frac{y_{.jp}}{n} - \frac{y_{..p}^2}{N}$$

Similarly,

$$S.S._{rows} = \sum_{i=1}^{n} \frac{y_{i.p}^2}{k} - \frac{y_{..p}}{N}$$

giving

$$S.S._{error} = S.S._{total} - S.S._{columns} - S.S._{rows}$$

The general ANOVA is shown in Table 5.6. The interpretation of this analysis will be made in Chapters 7 and 8

TABLE 5.6

General ANOVA Table for Experiment with Two Independent Variables

Source	S.S.	ν	M.S.
Columns	$\sum_{j=1}^{k} \dfrac{y_{.jp}^2}{n} - \dfrac{y_{..p}^2}{N}$	$k-1$	S.S./$(k-1)$
Rows	$\sum_{i=1}^{n} \dfrac{y_{i.p}^2}{k} - \dfrac{y_{..p}^2}{N}$	$n-1$	S.S./$(n-1)$
Error	$\sum_{j=1}^{k} \sum_{i=1}^{n} y_{ijp}^2 - \sum_{j=1}^{k} \dfrac{y_{.jp}^2}{n}$ $- \sum_{i=1}^{n} \dfrac{y_{i.p}^2}{k} + \dfrac{y_{..p}^2}{N}$	$N-k-n+1$	S.S./$(N-k-n+1)$
Total	$\sum_{j=1}^{k} \sum_{i=1}^{n} y_{ijp}^2 - \dfrac{y_{..p}^2}{N}$	$N-1$	

5.2.2   Example. An experiment was run to determine the effect of speed in rpm's and rate of feed in inches per revolution on the life, in hours, of a cutting tool. The data in Table 5.7 were collected. Calculate an ANOVA table for this experiment.

TABLE 5.7

Data for Example 5.2.2

Speed

In./Rev. \\ r.p.m.	100	120	140	160	180	Total
.005	16	22	24	29	28	119
.010	24	18	23	23	25	113
.015	11	27	10	13	18	79
.020	29	21	18	14	11	93
.025	16	21	21	29	14	101
Total	96	109	96	108	96	505

Feed

TABLE 5.8

Calculations for Example 5.2.2

r.p.m. In./Rev.	Speed					Total	Mean	(Total)²	$\frac{\text{Total}^2}{k}$
	100	120	140	160	180				
.005	16	22	24	29	28	119	23.8	14,161	2,832.2
.010	24	18	23	23	25	113	22.6	12,769	2,553.8
.015	11	27	10	13	18	79	15.8	6,241	1,248.2
.020	29	21	18	14	11	93	18.6	8,649	1,729.8
.025	16	21	21	29	14	101	20.2	10,201	2,040.2
Total	96	109	96	108	96	505			10,404.2
Mean	19.2	21.8	19.2	21.6	19.2		20.2		
Total²	9,216	11,881	9,216	11,664	9,216				
$\frac{\text{Total}^2}{n}$	1,843.2	2,376.2	1,843.2	2,332.8	1,843.2	10,238.6			

Feed

Solution: Calculations are shown in Table 5.8.
Calculate the sum of squares.

$$\text{Grand total} = \sum_{i=1}^{n} \sum_{j=1}^{k} y_{ijp} = 505$$

$$\text{Grand Mean} = \frac{y_{ijp}}{N} = \bar{y}_{..p} = \frac{505}{25} = 20.2$$

$$\text{Total Sum of Squares} = \sum_{i=1}^{n} \sum_{j=1}^{k} y_{ijp}^2 - \frac{y_{..p}^2}{N}$$

$$= (16)^2 + (24)^2 + (11)^2 + \ldots + (11)^2 + (14)^2$$
$$- \frac{(16 + 24 + 11 + \ldots + 11 + 14)^2}{25}$$

$$= 11{,}065 - 10{,}201$$
$$= 864$$

$$\text{Column Sum of Squares} = \sum_{j=1}^{k} \frac{y_{jp}^2}{n} - \frac{y_{..p}^2}{N}$$

$$= 10{,}238.6 - 10{,}201.0$$
$$= 37.6$$

$$\text{Row Sum of Squares} = \sum_{j=1}^{k} \frac{y_{i.p}^2}{k} - \frac{y_{..p}^2}{N}$$

$$= 10{,}404.2 - 10{,}201.0$$
$$= 203.2$$

$$\text{Error Sum of Squares} = 864 - 37.6 - 203.2$$
$$= 623.2$$

Giving the ANOVA in Table 5.9.

TABLE 5.9

ANOVA Table for Example 5.2.2

Source	S.S.	ν	M.S.
Column (speed)	37.6	$(k - 1) = 4$	9.4
Rows (feed)	203.2	$(n - 1) = 4$	50.8
Error	623.2	$(n - 1)(k - 1) = 16$	39.0
Total	864	$nk - 1 = 24$	

5.3 Exercises   (Data sets are in Appendix D.)

5.1. Compute the multiple linear regression of y on x_1 and x_2 for data set 2.

5.2. In Problem 5.1, compute the value of y when:

$$x_1 = 15$$
$$x_2 = 5$$

5.3. Compute the multiple linear regression of y on x_1, x_2, and x_3 for data set 2.

5.4. In Problem 5.3, compute the value of y when:

$$x_1 = 15$$
$$x_2 = 5$$
$$x_3 = 400$$

5.5. Perform an analysis of multiple linear regression variance for y versus x_1, x_2 and summarize an ANOVA table for data set 2.

5.6. Perform an analysis of multiple linear regression variance for y versus x_1, x_2, and x_3 and summarize in an ANOVA table for data set 2.

5.7. Conduct a two way analysis of variance on data set 4 where layers and position are considered the variables. State the model and construct the ANOVA table.

5.8. Perform the appropriate calculations on data set 5 to determine whether there is a difference among the specimens and whether there is an effect of the environment on the ultimate tensile strength of the adhesive. Use the most efficient technique applicable and show your results in an ANOVA.

CHAPTER 6

The Theory of Interpretation

The analysis of the experiments in Chapters 4 and 5 was concerned with the partitioning of the total experimental variance into its components, namely, that attributable to error and that attributable to sampling effects. The analytical methods that have been used are based on knowledge of theoretical data distributions and empirical sampling methods. Such methods have systematically produced results in a form that is conducive to *interpretation*.

6.1 Some Considerations in Formal Logic

Correct interpretation is such a pervasive and essential part of the scientific method that a consideration of certain matters in the field of formal logic seems to be essential. Formal *deductive logic* aids us in arriving at valid interpretations in the following ways:

1. It is often difficult, if not impossible, to determine the truth of a proposition directly. It is relatively easy to establish the truth of another proposition from which the one at issue can be deduced by using the principles of formal logic.

2. Many of our beliefs are formed to solve particular problems. We often find that these beliefs are quite inconsistent with one another. With

the methods of logic, such beliefs can be integrated and their bearings on one another made clearer by exploring their mutual relations deductively.

3. Deductive reasoning helps us to be consistent in our conclusions by helping us discover to what we must commit ourselves when we accept certain propositions. This is done by examining the connections between the diverse propositions which are considered. We may often be inclined to accept certain propositions without question when use of the principles of logic may uncover altogether surprising implications.

In pointing out these uses of formal logic, it is not denied that men may and do successfully employ it without any previous theoretical study. However, a rational technique is the basis of any theoretical science. In this way, logic enables us to formulate and partially structure the processes employed in successful inquiry. Actual attainment of validity depends, of course, upon individual skill and habit, but a careful study of logical principles helps us to form and perfect techniques for procuring and weighing evidence.

6.1.1 The Nature of Facts.

To interpret analytical results is to provide some form of *reflection* about the *meaning* or *significance* of the results. Much of our human activity takes place without any reflection or questioning. But in the case of a specific engineering objective or inquiry, our habitual attitudes are challenged by unexpected changes in environment, by our own curiosity, or by the inquisitiveness of others.

Scientific method is dedicated to the discovery of true *facts*. The facts, however, cannot be known without reflection. We cannot equate facts to the brute immediacy of our sensations. Our sensory experience can determine the problem for which knowledge is sought, but reflective analysis and interpretation must supplement this experience before knowledge is gained.

Every engineering investigation arises from some previous problem. Such investigations are determined as a result of selecting and sifting the subject matter of the problem. Such selection requires some form of preconceived prejudice, a *hypothesis*, which guides the research and delineates the subject matter of inquiry. Every investigation is specific in the sense that it has a definite problem to solve and the solution terminates the inquiry. To collect "facts" in an engineering environment without a specifically defined problem would be to violate the basic engineering role in society. In many engineering projects the definition and formulation of the problem is often the most critical phase of the investigative process. Often, the proper definition of the problem directly produces its solution.

A "fact" is a proposition or concept for whose truth there is considerable evidence. A *hypothesis* is a formalization of a new concept or proposition in relation to an immediate investigation. An *experiment* is the process by which necessary information is acquired to test the hypothesis. The *analysis* of the experiment is a systematic evaluation of the experimental evidence. The *interpretation* of that data is the process of determining if the evidence is sufficient to confirm the truth of the original hypothesis.

What we consider to be "fact" at any one time, therefore, depends upon the stage of inquiry we may be in at the time. There is no sharp line between fact and hypothesis. During any inquiry, the status of a proposition may change from that of hypothesis to that of fact, or from that of fact to that of hypothesis. Every so-called fact, therefore, may be challenged because of the evidence on which it is asserted to be a fact.

6.1.2   The Nature of Proof. Mathematics is a field in which *proof* is essential. A distinction, however, should be made between pure and applied mathematics, the latter being the primary concern of engineering. In applied mathematics we assume that certain propositions, such as the laws of mechanics, are *true*, and we prove the *truth* of other propositions by showing that they necessarily follow the original assumptions. In pure mathematics we restrict ourselves to demonstrating that our assumptions imply the theorems which are deduced from them. Pure mathematics ignores the question of whether our conclusions as well as our axioms are *in fact* true.

A proposition is therefore *proved* only when that proposition and its assumptions are true. A proposition is not proven in this sense when a case only establishes an implication or necessary connection between premises and their conclusion. Such a conclusion is more properly said to be a *deduction*.

The deductive process that leads us to certain conclusions that were implied by established premises is called *inference*. We infer one proposition from another validly only if there is an objective relation of implication between the first proposition and the second. An implication can, however, exist without the existence of an inference since an implication is a relationship between the elements of the premises.

For example, in a particular experiment there can be a strong implication that a particular heat treatment improves the machining characteristics of an alloy. This would be implied from past experience and knowledge of heat treatment processes and machining qualities of the alloy. However, even though this conclusion is implied, it cannot be considered "true" until it is deductively reasoned or inferred from specific evidence in this case.

6.1.3   The Nature of Cause and Effect. Theoretically speaking, every event in nature is unique and can never be observed *exactly* again. In the real world of engineering practice, however, some events are so intimately similar in certain selected features that they are considered to be similar or identical. In many practical situations we also know that many such events *occur in pairs*. By this we mean that when the first event occurs, the second accompanies or follows it. In such cases the first event is considered to be the *cause* of the second and the second event is called the *effect*.

The relationship is found to be more complex than this in practice. The central problem lies in the fact that two events occurring in pairs can be independently related but both dependent upon a third event acting as the cause. In previous chapters we have considered the relationship of *dependent* and *independent variables*. A dependent variable is considered to be the *effect* in an experiment, and the independent variables are assumed to be the *causes*. These relationships would be implied until experimental evidence serves as a basis for deductively reasoning a relationship between the variables.

6.1.4   The Nature of Evidence. The scientific method is not satisfied with psychological certitude, for the mere intensity with which a belief is held is no guarantee of its truth. Logical and adequate grounds is demanded and sought through the experimental process. We have so far discussed the relation between premises and conclusions in the cases involving rigorous proof. However, complete or conclusive evidence is rarely, if ever, available in an engineering investigation, and we must generally rely upon partial or incomplete evidence.

Where the evidence in favor of a proposition is partial or incomplete, the *probability* of the inference may be increased by additional evidence. Considering a sample in an experiment as the medium by which evidence is produced, we can conclude that the probability of an inference is increased as the sample size is increased.

Let us now consider two cases in which evidence is given interpretation: (1) An argument of high probability leads to a generalization or induction, and (2) where such argument leads to what is called a *presumption of fact*.

The first case is illustrated by the experimental process in which the results of particular samples are used to make generalized statements about the phenomena. Such generalizations, however, frequently turn out to be false, for the responses selected may not be typical or representative. We try to overcome such doubt by using the inferred rule as a premise or hypothesis that consists of a statement about other responses under different conditions. Should the observed result in the sample responses agree with the deduction from our assumed rule, the probability that the rule is true would be increased. On the other hand, should there be considerable disagreement between our general rule and what we find in the sample result, the rule would have to be modified in accordance with the general principle of deductive reasoning. Thus, while generalizations from what we suppose to be representative samples sometimes lead to false conclusions, such generalizations enable us to arrive frequently at conclusions which are true in proportion to the care with which our generalization is formulated and tested.

In the second form of probable inference, we are led to deduce a fact not directly observable. This form of inference is very widespread in the engineering field as well as in the natural sciences and practical affairs. We know, for example, that chemical elements combine according to fixed ratios (the observed event). We know also that if each of these substances were composed of mechanically indivisible particles, the substances would combine in proportion to their weight (the general rule). We conclude then that these substances are composed of atoms (the inferred fact). From the standpoint of necessary implication, the inferred fact is not true, for it is quite possible that the observed facts may be due to some other cause than the assumed atomic structure. However, our evidence has a very high degree of probability because we have used the general proposition successfully in a variety of applications and it has proven itself to be valid.

6.1.5   The Nature of Hypotheses. An investigator determines *hypotheses* when they are suggested by some observation in the subject matter of a current investigation and by his previous knowledge of the subject. Hypotheses serve as the objectives of experimentation and are required at every stage of an inquiry. The number of hypotheses that are possible in any investigation is unlimited. They are concerned with the suggested connections between actual facts or imagined ones. Statements of hypothesis are as follows: There has been no true increase in line voltage. The mean expansion rate has not changed. The temperature of the system is greater than 150° C.

Hypotheses are tested by an evaluation of the evidence obtained from an experiment. As stated previously, the validity of such evidence is generally related to the care with which the experiment was designed and the volume of evidence obtained. No hypothesis that states a general proposition can be demonstrated as absolutely true. We have seen that all inquiry which deals with matters of fact employs *probable inference*.

6.2   Interpretation of Probability

The mathematical theory of probability studies the necessary consequences of our assumptions about a set of alternative possibilities. It cannot inform us as to the probability of an actual event. The question therefore follows as to how the probability of such events is to be determined. Such a determination can be made in three basic ways:

(1) probability as a measure of belief,
(2) probability as relative frequency,
(3) probability as truth frequency.

6.2.1   Probability as a Measure of Belief. Mathematical theory of probability can answer the question as to the probability of getting one head in three tosses of a coin when such information is supplied as (1) the number of alternative ways the coin can fall, (2) the equiprobability of these alternatives, and (3) the independence of the different throws. When probability is considered *as a measure of belief*, this information is obtained quite easily. In such cases the *principle of insufficient reason* or the *principle of indifference* is used. This principle says that if there is no known reason for choosing one alternative over another in a problem, then the assertion of each alternative has an equal probability. Further, if there is no known reason for believing that two events are independent rather than dependent, it is just as probable that they are one as the other.

6.2.2   Probability as Relative Frequency. When probability is considered as relative frequency and we say that the probability of a given coin falling heads is one-half, we mean that as the number of tosses increases indefinitely, the ratio between the number of heads and the total number of tosses will approach one-half. Such a statement constitutes a hypothesis as to the course of nature and it would require evidence. Such evidence could be rational (based on prior knowledge) or statistical.

Such a hypothesis as to the nature of things asserts something in regard to all possible phenomena or members of a given class. It can, therefore, never be completely proven by any number of finite observations. But if we have several hypotheses, the one that agrees best with observable truths that are statistically formulated is naturally preferable.

From this point of view we can understand more clearly the function of the mathematical theory of probability. For example, suppose that the probability of getting a compressive measurement on a precast concrete beam of 3,200 psi is 0.35 under certain conditions. Suppose that in measuring ten beams under the same conditions the compressive strength was found to be greater than 3,200 psi in *each case*. Does this disprove the assumption that the probability is 0.35? Not at all. It can be determined mathematically that such an occurrence is *extremely improbable* but not impossible. However, it may be possible to demonstrate that such an actual "exceptional" occurrence is in greater conformity with, or less probable than, some other assumption. A large number of repetitions of "exceptional" occurrences may thus increase the probability of some other hypothesis, and diminish the probability of our original one. No hypothesis concerning the probability of an event can be absolutely refuted by a finite number of observations. Very large discrepancies from theoretically probable results are not impossible. However, statistical results can show some hypotheses to be more probable than others.

6.2.3   Probability as the Truth-Frequency of Types of Arguments. Instead of talking about a class of events, the *truth-frequency theory* discusses a class of assumptions. Instead of dealing with events such as "heads," the truth-frequency theory discusses the proposition that the coin will fall head uppermost on the next throw. This theory considers it clear that the relative frequency with which the coin is thrown under specific conditions on toss n must be the same as the relative frequency with which the "heads" occur in a series of tosses with the coin. This theory is related to a subject of later concern in this book.

6.3   Statistical Inference

When no information is available for statistical analysis, the determination of probability as a measure of belief is the method that must be used. We are concerned, however, with experimental situations in which quantitative evidence has been collected and analyzed. In such cases, we use the relative-frequency and truth-frequency methods for interpreting experimental data. No method of analysis can extract more information from a set of responses than is contained by them. No method, statistical or otherwise, can draw conclusions from experimental data with zero risk or error.

The process of reasoning from the general case to the particular case—deductive reasoning—has been discussed as the method of determining hypotheses. We are now concerned with the opposite process.

Suppose we are given a hypothesis and evidence has been obtained by experimentation to test the hypothesis. The process of drawing general conclusions about the nature of things by reasoning from a particular case is called *inductive reasoning*. Such reasoning is called *statistical inference* when it is related to statistical data and concerned with the *probable* truth of a hypothesis or proposition.

A statistical or probable inference, like all inferences, is based upon certain relationships between propositions. No proposition is probable *within itself*.

Whether a proposition has or has not a degree of probability or definite evidence does not depend on the state of mind of the person who entertains the proposition. Questions of probable relation between a general case and an observed particular case should be decided entirely by inductive reasoning or statistical inference. There are several theories for doing this; two will be dealt with here.

6.4   The Neyman-Pearson Theory of Inference

Using the relative-frequency method of probability, the *Neyman-Pearson Theory* of statistical inference is centered around the statistical hypothesis. Such a hypothesis, in statistical terms, is an assumption about the frequency function of a random variable. A test of a statistical hypothesis is a procedure for deciding whether to accept or reject the hypothesis.

The first step in this procedure is to formulate a statistical hypothesis with the purpose of rejecting or nullifying it. Such hypotheses are usually called *null hypotheses* and are denoted by H_0. An *alternate hypothesis* to the null hypothesis is then established and denoted as H_1. Thus the problem of statistical inference is to test the hypothesis H_0 against the alternative H_1.

6.4.1   Levels of Significance. Before the experiment is run and the evidence observed, it is necessary to decide in advance what *level of significance* is to be used. This level of significance is the risk the investigator is willing to take by rejecting the null hypothesis when it is actually true. This kind of error is called a Type I error or an *error of the first kind*, and is denoted as α.

This α risk can be made as small as desired by changing the level of significance. However, as the α risk is reduced, the risk of missing real effects of a variable becomes larger, all else being equal. This Type II error or *error of the second kind*, denoted as β, is the risk of accepting a hypothesis as true when it is actually false. Figure 6.1 illustrates the relationship

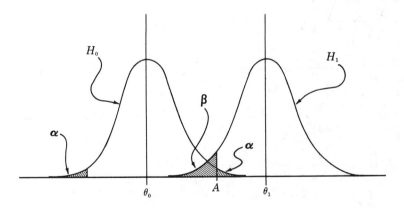

Fig. 6.1.   The Relationship Between α and β Risk.

between α and β risk. In this table the distribution on the left represents the null hypothesis H_0 with a true value of Θ_0. The risk, α, is shown on each end of this distribution. The distribution on the right represents the alternate hypothesis H_1 with a true value of Θ_1. The intersection A represents the point at which H_0 can be rejected with α risk and accepted with β risk.

The choice of the α and β risks should be made *prior* to conducting the experiment. If such is not done and adhered to, it becomes easier for an unusual result to be dismissed according to the bias of the investigator. The choice of significance levels should depend on the penalties for errors of the first and second kinds and on the expectation of different results as determined by prior knowledge. If rejection of the null hypothesis when it is true would cause a catastrophic result, the α value should be set quite small. On the other hand, it may be that the acceptance of the null hypothesis when it is false carries with it an even greater penalty. In situations where both α and β must be low, say 0.001, the number and accuracy of observations must be increased. Generally, the levels of significance vary between 0.10 and 0.001.

It should be noted that to "accept" a null hypothesis does not mean that the hypothesis has been proven. The conclusion merely says that if the hypothesis is false, the experiment was not able to detect it at the established level of significance.

The two quantities, α and β, are somewhat opposed to each other. For

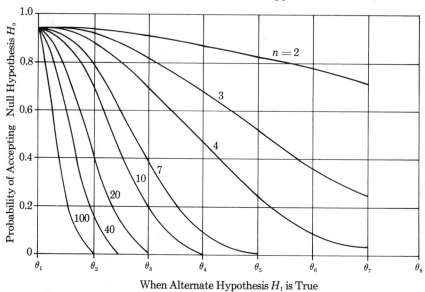

Fig. 6.2. Typical Operating Characteristic Curve for an Assumed θ_0 and α

a given sample size, a reduction in α will cause an increase in β. If, however, the size of the sample is increased, both kinds of error could be decreased. Improved techniques of experimentation will also make a reduction in risks possible.

6.4.2   Power of a Test. An error of a second kind, β, can always be avoided by never accepting null hypotheses as true. In many situations, however, this cannot be done.

Most decision problems involve more than one alternative hypothesis, H_1. If we let Θ be the true value of the parameter in question, we can state a hypothesis thus:

$$H_0: \Theta = 0$$
$$H_1: \Theta \leq 5$$
$$H_1: \Theta \leq 4$$

giving a case of a null hypothesis with two alternate hypotheses.

The error of a second kind, β, is therefore not a constant. It depends upon the true value of the parameter in question. Thus, for the true value Θ, then β is a direct function of Θ. The graph of this function is called an *operating characteristic curve* (Fig. 6.2). An example of its use is presented in Chapter 8.

6.5   Confidence Intervals as Inference

When probability is considered to be *truth-frequency*, the method of inductive reasoning is accomplished with *confidence intervals*. In this method, intervals are calculated for a given parameter, say Θ, based upon the information from an experiment. Such limits require that an α risk be determined. The limits would then constitute a "tolerance" outside of which the true value Θ would not be expected to fall, with a risk of α. Examples of this method will also be presented in Chapters 7 and 8.

CHAPTER 7

Interpretation of Variances

Chapters 4 and 5 were concerned with basic experimental models and the methods associated with the analysis of the variances in such experiments. Chapter 6 was concerned with the problems related to drawing logical conclusions from such analyses. In this chapter we will study specific methods associated with the interpretation of experimental variance, utilizing both the information derived from the analysis of the experiment and the methods of testing hypotheses. The variances were calculated in the ANOVA as mean squares. To draw a conclusion about them we must determine their characteristics. We will first determine the distribution of mean squares by demonstrating their relationship to the χ^2 distribution.

7.1 The Distribution of Mean Squares

If we should toss a coin n number of times and observe the number of occurrences of heads, m, we can express the difference between the observed and expected frequencies as a quantity defined as

$$\chi^2 = \frac{(m - pn)^2}{pn} \tag{7.1}$$

where, in the case of the coin, p is the probability of a head occurring.

If in 100 tosses of a coin we observed 50 heads, we calculate Eq. (7.1) as

$$\chi^2 = \frac{(m - pn)^2}{pn} = \frac{[50 - 0.5(100)]^2}{0.5(100)} = 0$$

indicating that the observed frequencies were in exact agreement with expectation. As the observed values deviate from 50 in either direction, the amount of agreement with expectation is reduced. If we should repeat the toss of 100 coins a large number of times and the χ^2 were calculated each time, a *distribution* of χ^2 values could be determined. Such a distribution will assume the general form shown in Fig. 7.1 for various degrees of freedom.

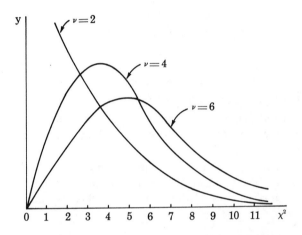

Fig. 7.1. A General Form of the χ^2 Distribution

A general frequency function for the continuous variable χ^2 is given by

$$f(\chi^2) = \frac{(\chi^2)^{(\nu/2)-1}e^{-\chi^2/2}}{2^{\nu/2}\Gamma(\nu/2)} \tag{7.2}$$

where ν is the number of degrees of freedom and is given by $\nu = k - 1$, where k is the number of levels of a variable in a given experiment. $\Gamma(\nu/2)$ is the gamma function of $(\nu/2)^*$. Appendix F gives the areas under the χ^2 curve. Its use is discussed in Appendix C.

---

* The gamma function is defined:

$$\Gamma(\nu/2) = [(\nu/2) - 1]!$$
$$= \begin{cases} [(\nu/2) - 1][(\nu/2) - 2] \ldots 3 \cdot 2 \cdot 1 & \text{(for } \nu \text{ even and } \nu > 2) \\ [(\nu/2) - 1][(\nu/2) - 2] \ldots (3/2)(1/2)\sqrt{\pi} & \text{(for } \nu \text{ odd and } \nu > 2) \end{cases}$$

The moment generating function for χ^2 can be determined by the methods similar to those used in Chapter 2 and is given by

$$M_{\chi^2}(\Theta) = (1 - 2\Theta)^{-\nu/2} \qquad (7.3)$$

Given, from Eq. (3.24), that the moment generating function of the sum of n independent variables is equal to the product of the moment generating function of the individual variables, that is

$$M_{x_1+...+x_n}(\Theta) = M_{x_1}(\Theta)M_{x_2}(\Theta) ... M_{x_n}(\Theta) \qquad (7.4)$$

we can demonstrate that the sum of a number of χ^2 distributions is also χ^2 distributed. Therefore, from Eqs. (7.3) and (7.4), the variable

$$\omega = \chi_1^2 + \chi_2^2$$

has the following moment generating function

$$
\begin{aligned}
M_\omega(\Theta) &= M_{\chi_1^2}(\Theta)M_{\chi_2^2}(\Theta) \\
&= (1 - 2\Theta)^{-\nu_1/2}(1 - 2\Theta)^{-\nu_2/2} \\
&= (1 - 2\Theta)^{-\frac{\nu_1+\nu_2}{2}} \qquad (7.5)
\end{aligned}
$$

which is of the same form as Eq. (7.3). We can therefore observe that if χ_1^2, and χ_2^2 are independent χ^2 distributions with ν_1 and ν_2 degrees of freedom, respectively, then $\chi_1^2 + \chi_2^2$ will be χ^2 distributed with $\nu_1 + \nu_2$ degrees of freedom.

Our next concern is to determine the distribution of a sum of squares. If we should let x be normally distributed with a mean of zero and variance of one, the sum of squares of n responses from this distribution becomes

$$\text{S.S.} = \sum_{i=1}^{n} x_i^2 \qquad (7.6)$$

The moment generating function technique will be used to derive the frequency function of Eq. (7.6). Since x_i is from a random sample,

$$
\begin{aligned}
M_{\text{S.S.}}(\Theta) &= M_{x_1^2+...+x_n^2}(\Theta) \\
&= M_{x_1^2}(\Theta)M_{x_2^2}(\Theta) ... M_{x_n^2}(\Theta) \qquad (7.7)
\end{aligned}
$$

Since x is a standard normal variable,

$$
\begin{aligned}
M_{x^2}(\Theta) &= \tfrac{1}{2}\pi \int_{-\infty}^{\infty} e^{\Theta x^2} \cdot e^{-x^2/2} \, dx \\
&= \tfrac{1}{2}\pi \int_{-\infty}^{\infty} e^{-(x^2/2)(1-2\Theta)} \, dx
\end{aligned}
$$

If $y = x\sqrt{1 - 2\Theta}$, then this integral becomes

$$
\begin{aligned}
M_{x^2}(\Theta) &= (1 - 2\Theta)^{-1/2} \frac{1}{\sqrt{2\pi}} \int_{-\infty}^{\infty} e^{-y^2/2} \, dy \\
&= (1 - 2\Theta)^{-1/2}
\end{aligned}
$$

and from Eq. (7.7), the moment generating function for Eq. (7.6) becomes

$$M_{S.S.}(\Theta) = (1 - 2\Theta)^{-n/2} \qquad (7.8)$$

which is the same form as Eq. (7.3). We can therefore observe that the sum of squares for a random variable x has a χ^2 distribution with $n - 1$ degrees of freedom.

It can be shown that if two sums of squares, say S.S.$_1$ and S.S.$_2$, have independent χ^2 distributions with ν_1 and ν_2 degrees of freedom, respectively; then

$$F = \frac{S.S._1/\nu_1}{S.S._2/\nu_2} = \frac{M.S._1}{M.S._2} \qquad (7.9)$$

has the F distribution with ν_1 and ν_2 degrees of freedom given by

$$f(F) = cF^{\frac{\nu_1-2}{2}} (\nu_2 + \nu_1 F)^{-\frac{\nu_1+\nu_2}{2}} \qquad (7.10)$$

and whose general form is illustrated in Fig. 7.2.

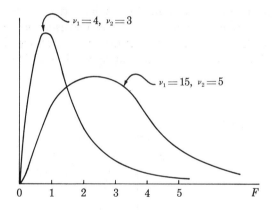

Fig. 7.2.   General Form of F Distribution

7.2   The Distribution of a Random Variable When σ Is Unknown

In the interpretation of regression variance, and later for sample means, the situation often arises when the standard deviation of a random variable is not known and must be estimated. In Example 3.3.2 it was observed for samples of large size n, that $\hat{s}$ is an unbiased estimate of σ. If n is small (often considered < 30), then $\hat{s}$ is a *biased* estimate of σ, and the distribution of a random variable in such a case is described by *Student's* t distribution*.

---

* The pen name of its developer, W. S. Gossett.

The general form of the t distribution is given by

$$f(t) = c\left(1 + \frac{t^2}{\nu}\right)^{-\frac{\nu+1}{2}} \tag{7.11}$$

When given, without proof, that

$$z = \frac{\bar{y} - \mu}{\sigma/\sqrt{n}} \tag{7.12}$$

is normally distributed with zero mean and unit variance and

$$\chi^2 = \frac{(n-1)\hat{s}^2}{\sigma^2} \tag{7.13}$$

is χ^2 distributed with ν degrees of freedom, and, Eqs. (7.12) and (7.13) are independently distributed, then

$$t = \frac{(\bar{y} - \mu)}{\hat{s}/\sqrt{n}} \tag{7.14}$$

is a t-distributed variable. This random variable is a function of $\hat{s}$. It is useful for cases where σ is not given and must be estimated by $\hat{s}$. A table for the areas under the curve of the t distribution is provided in Appendix H. Its use and interpretation is similar to Appendix E for the normal dis-

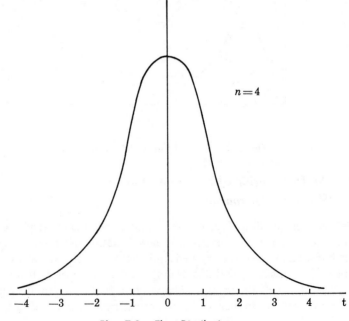

Fig. 7.3. The t Distribution.

tribution except that ν, the degrees of freedom, must be known. Notice that as $\nu \to \infty$, the values t_α approach those of z_α. At the bottom line of Appendix H ($\nu = \infty$), note that the values for t_α are identical to those for z_α.

7.3 Interpretation of Experimental Variance When Levels of Variable Are Not Predetermined

In Chapter 4, we studied methods of estimating the value for a dependent variable by determining its regression relationship to one or more independent variables. The linear regression variance for a dependent variable y and a single independent variable x was summarized in an ANOVA table as in Table 7.1.

TABLE 7.1

Analysis of Linear Regression Variance

Source of Variation	S.S.	ν	M.S.
Due to Regression	$b_1^2 \sum_{i=1}^{n} (x_i - \bar{x})^2$	1	$b_1^2 \sum_{i=1}^{n} (x_i - \bar{x})^2$
About Regression	$\sum_{i=1}^{n} (y_i - \bar{y})^2 - b_1^2 (x_i - \bar{x})^2$	$n - 2$	$\sum_{i=1}^{n} (y_i - \bar{y})^2 - b_1^2 \dfrac{(x_i - \bar{x})^2}{n - 2}$
Total	$\sum_{i=1}^{n} (y_i - \bar{y})^2$	$n - 1$	

Given that the sum of squares due to regression and about regression have independent χ^2 distributions with 1 and $n - 2$ degrees of freedom, respectively, we can calculate

$$F = \frac{(n - 2)b_1^2 \sum_{i=1}^{n} (x_i - \bar{x})^2}{\sum_{i=1}^{n} (y_i - \bar{y})^2 - b_1^2 \sum_{i=1}^{n} (x_i - \bar{x})^2} \tag{7.15}$$

which is the F distribution. We can test the hypothesis

$$H_0: \ y \text{ is independent of } x$$

by comparing the calculated F in a particular case with the critical F number determined from Appendix G for an assumed level of α. If the calculated value exceeds the table value, we would *reject* the hypothesis H_0 with a risk of α.

7.3.1   Example. In Example 4.1.6 of Chapter 4, the results of the regression analysis for tensile strength of copper wire on hardness are summarized in Table 7.2.

TABLE 7.2

An ANOVA Table for Example 7.3.1

Source of Variation	S.S.	ν	M.S.
Due to Regression	64,348,979.66	1	64,348,979.66
About Regression	2,627,020.34	8	328,377.54
Total	66,976,000.00	9	

The F number is calculated as

$$F = \frac{64,348,979.66}{328,377.54} = 195.96$$

To test the hypothesis H_0, that tensile strength of copper wire is independent of its hardness, we choose an $\alpha = .01$ and refer to Appendix G. Setting ν_n, the degrees of freedom for the sum of squares in the numerator, equal to 1 and setting ν_0, the degrees of freedom for the sum of squares in the denominator, equal to 8, we find the critical F number to be 11.26 for an $\alpha = .01$. Since the calculated F number 195.96 is greater than this table value, we can reject the hypothesis H_0, that the tensile strength of wire is independent of its hardness. We can say then, with considerable confidence, that some of the variance in the tensile strength of copper wire can be attributed to the variance in the hardness of the wire. Our next concern is to determine *how well* the dependence of y is linearly related to x.

7.3.2   The Coefficient of Correlation. The degree of linear dependence that y has on x is measured by the *coefficients of determination and correlation*. These coefficients will be explained by considering the characteristic of a joint frequency function.*

If two random variables, x and y, are normally and independently distributed, their joint frequency function can be written as

$$f(x, y) = \frac{e^{-\frac{1}{2}\left(\frac{x-\mu_x}{\sigma_x}\right)^2}}{\sqrt{2\pi}\,\sigma_x} \cdot \frac{e^{-\frac{1}{2}\left(\frac{y-\mu_y}{\sigma_y}\right)}}{\sqrt{2\pi}\,\sigma_y} = \frac{e^{-\frac{1}{2}\left[\left(\frac{x-\mu_x}{\sigma_x}\right)+\left(\frac{y-\mu_y}{\sigma_y}\right)\right]}}{2\pi\sigma_x\sigma_y} \tag{7.16}$$

* Appendix B, page 164.

If the variables are *not* independent, it is necessary to modify Eq. (7.16) to account for their dependence. This is done by introducing a cross product term so that when x and y are independent its coefficient becomes zero. Such a modification of Eq. (7.16) gives

$$f(x, y) = \frac{e^{-\frac{1}{2(1-\rho)}\left[\left(\frac{x-\mu_x}{\sigma_x}\right)-2\rho\left(\frac{x-\mu_x}{\sigma_x}\right)\left(\frac{y-\mu_y}{\sigma_y}\right)+\left(\frac{y-\mu_y}{\sigma_y}\right)^2\right]}}{2\pi\sigma_x\sigma_y\sqrt{1-\rho^2}} \tag{7.17}$$

where $-1 < \rho < 1$.

In Eq. (7.17), when $\rho = 0$ (y is independent of x), the cross product term drops out and Eq. (7.17) becomes equal to Eq. (7.16). The parameter, ρ, is therefore the measure of *dependence* of y on x and is called the *true coefficient of correlation*. The square of this parameter, ρ^2, is known as the *coefficient of determination* and measures the proportion of the variation in y that can be attributed to x.

The coefficient of determination for a given set of sample data is, from Table 7.1,

$$r^2 = \frac{\text{S.S.}_{\text{due to regression}}}{\text{S.S.}_{\text{total}}} = 1 - \frac{\text{S.S.}_{\text{about regression}}}{\text{S.S.}_{\text{total}}}$$

which is the ratio of the sum of squares for y responses that can be attributed to the x responses (due to regression) to the total sum of squares of the y responses. The coefficient r^2 is therefore the proportion of the total sum of squares of the y responses that can be attributed to the x responses.

The coefficient of correlation for a set of data is therefore

$$r = \pm\sqrt{1 - \frac{\text{S.S.}_{\text{about reg.}}}{\text{S.S.}_{\text{total}}}}$$

and varies between -1 and 1. The $\pm$ signs are used to indicate direct or positive correlation and inverse or negative correlation. If the sum of squares due to regression is zero, r^2 and r are zero. If the sum of squares about the regression is zero, r^2 and r equal unity.

In general terms, from Table 7.1, this coefficient of correlation can be written as

$$r = \pm\sqrt{1 - \frac{\sum_{i=1}^{n}(y_i - \bar{y})^2 - b_1^2(x_i - \bar{x})^2}{\sum_{i=1}^{n}(y_i - \bar{y})^2}} \tag{7.18}$$

7.3.3   Example. In Example 7.3.1, r^2 is calculated from Eq. (7.18) to be

$$r^2 = \frac{64,348,979.66}{66,976,000.00} = .962$$

indicating that approximately 96.2 per cent of the sum of squares for y can be attributed to the sum of squares of x.

7.3.4   The Distribution of r. For large values of ρ, the distribution of r is considerably non-normal (see Fig. 7.4). We are able, however, to transform

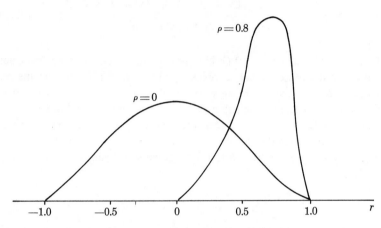

Fig. 7.4.   Distribution of r When $n = 9$

the distribution of r into an approximately normal distribution. This rather complex change of variable is from r to z', where

$$z' = \tfrac{1}{2} \log_e \frac{1 + r}{1 - r} \tag{7.19}$$

will be approximately normally distributed with mean

$$\mu_{z'} = \tfrac{1}{2} \log_e \frac{1 + \rho}{1 - \rho} \tag{7.20}$$

and standard deviation

$$\sigma_{z'} = 1/\sqrt{n - 3} \tag{7.21}$$

The standard normal variate, Eq. (2.39), in this case becomes

$$z = \frac{z' - \mu_{z'}}{\sigma_{z'}} \tag{7.22}$$

7.3.5   Example. In Example 7.3.3, determine if there is a significant correlation between tensile strength and hardness of copper wire.

Solution: We will test the hypothesis

$$H_0: \rho = 0; \qquad H_1: \rho \neq 0$$

Calculate z' from Eq. (7.19) thus:

$$z' = \tfrac{1}{2} \log_e \frac{1+r}{1-r} = \tfrac{1}{2} \log_e \frac{1.981}{0.019}$$
$$= 2.27$$

since $r = \sqrt{0.962} = 0.981$.

From Eq. (7.20),

$$\mu_{z'} = \tfrac{1}{2} \log_e \frac{1+\rho}{1-\rho} = \tfrac{1}{2} \log_e 1 = 0$$

and from Eq. (7.21), with $n = 10$,

$$\sigma_{z'} = 1/\sqrt{n-3} = 1/\sqrt{7} = 0.378$$

giving, from Eq. (7.22), that

$$z = \frac{z' - \mu_{z'}}{\sigma_{z'}} = \frac{2.27 - 0}{.378} = 6.01$$

For $\alpha = .05$, the critical value for z from Appendix E, using a two-tail test, is 1.96. Since the calculated value exceeds the critical value ($6.01 > 1.96$), we reject H_0 and conclude that the dependence of tensile strength of copper wire on hardness is significant.

7.3.6 Standard Error of the Regression Estimate. In Chapter 4, the linear regression estimate, y_i', for one independent variable was shown in Eq. (4.2) to be

$$y_i' = b_0 + b_1 x_i \qquad (7.23)$$

with the origin at $(0, 0)$. Since the point $(\bar{x}, \bar{y})$ lies on the regression line (Fig. 4.1), the above equation can be written

$$y_i' = \bar{y} + b_1(x_i - \bar{x}) \qquad (7.24)$$

with the origin shifted to $(\bar{x}, \bar{y})$. Given that $\bar{y}$ and b are independent (without proof), it follows from Eq. (3.11) that

$$s_{y_i'}^2 = s_{\bar{y}}^2 + (x_i - \bar{x})^2 s_{b_1}^2 \qquad (7.25)$$

where $s_{y_i'}^2$ is the variance of the regression estimate. From Eq. (3.34) we know that the variance of the mean

$$s_{\bar{y}}^2 = \frac{\sigma^2}{n} \qquad (7.26)$$

where σ^2 is the true variance about regression. The variance of the regression coefficient is given as

$$s_{b_1}^2 = \frac{\sigma^2}{\sum\limits_{i=1}^{n} (x_i - \bar{x})^2} \qquad (7.27)$$

and will not be proven. Therefore, from Eq. (7.25),

$$s_{y_i'}^2 = \frac{\sigma^2}{n} + \frac{(x_i - \bar{x})^2 \sigma^2}{\sum\limits_{i=1}^{n} (x_i - \bar{x})^2} \tag{7.28}$$

and

$$s_{y_i'} = \sigma \sqrt{\frac{1}{n} + \frac{(x_i - \bar{x})^2}{\sum\limits_{i=1}^{n} (x_i - \bar{x})^2}} \tag{7.29}$$

the *standard error* of the regression estimate. From Eq. (7.29), it can be seen that the error is at a minimum when $x_i = \bar{x}$, and increases as x_i deviates from $\bar{x}$.

7.3.7 Confidence Limits for the Regression Estimate. When σ is known, the confidence limits of the interval for y_i' are

$$y_i' \pm z_\alpha \sigma \sqrt{\frac{1}{n} + \frac{(x_i - \bar{x})^2}{\sum\limits_{i=1}^{n} (x - \bar{x})^2}} \tag{7.30}$$

where z_α is the critical value of the standardized normal variate z for a given α. If the true variance about regression is not known and must be estimated, Eq. (7.30) becomes

$$y_i' \pm t_\alpha \hat{s} \sqrt{\frac{1}{n} + \frac{(x_i - \bar{x})^2}{\sum\limits_{i=1}^{n} (x_i - \bar{x})^2}} \tag{7.31}$$

7.3.8 Example. For the copper wire example, what are the 90 per cent confidence limits for the true regression estimate of tensile strength for a Brinell hardness of 102?

Solution: The true variance about regression is not known and is estimated in Table 7.2 to be 328,377.54 (M.S. about regression). For 90 per cent confidence limits, $\alpha = .10$. With 8 degrees of freedom (Table 7.2) the critical value from Appendix H is

$$t_\alpha = 1.86$$

From Example 4.1.3, page 60, it was determined that the regression estimate of tensile strength when $x = 102$ is

$$y' = 34,123 \text{ psi}$$

Therefore, from Eq. (7.31) we have

$$y' \pm t_\alpha \hat{s} \sqrt{\frac{1}{n} + \frac{(x_i - \bar{x})^2}{\sum x^2 - \dfrac{(\sum x)^2}{n}}}$$

Substituting

$$34{,}123 \pm (1.86)(\sqrt{328{,}377.54})\sqrt{\frac{1}{10} + \frac{(102 - 104.2)^2}{200.2 - 176.4}}$$

we get the confidence limits

$$34{,}123 \pm 586$$

Figure 7.5 shows the general 90 per cent confidence limits for the regression of tensile strength on the hardness of copper wire.

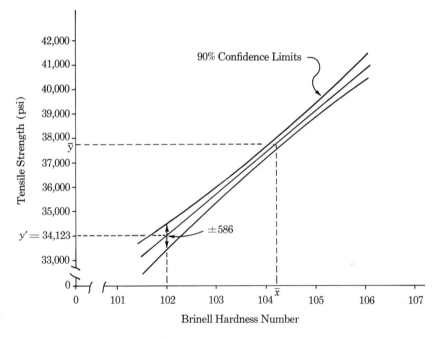

Fig. 7.5. 90 Per Cent Confidence Limits for the Regression of Tensile Strength on Hardness of Copper Wire

7.3.9 Curvilinear and Multiple Correlation. The discussion has been limited to the interpretation of the linear relationship between a dependent variable y and a single independent variable x. We will now be concerned with interpretation of the *curvilinear* relationship between y and x and the *multiple* relationship between y and $x_1, x_2, x_3 \ldots, x_p$ independent variables. These will be treated together because of the convenient similarity between the two measurements. The subscripts, $1, 2, 3, \ldots, p$, in Eq. (4.18) refer to the successive powers of x, namely, $x^1, x^2, \ldots, x^p$ in a curvilinear regression problem. The same subscripts in Eq. (5.9) refer to the successive number of independent variables, namely, $x_1, x_2, x_3, \ldots, x_p$. In both cases the y subscript refers to the dependent variable y.

The *coefficient of curvilinear correlation* is given by

$$R_{y \cdot 123 \ldots p} = \pm \sqrt{1 - \frac{\text{S.S.}_{\text{about regression}}}{\text{S.S.}_{\text{total}}}} \qquad (7.32)$$

being analogous to Eq. (7.18), where the subscript, 123 .. p, refers to the successive coefficients of the independent variable x. Equation (7.32) can also serve as the coefficient of linear multiple correlation when the subscript, 123 .. p, refers to p independent variables that are linearly related. The sum-of-square terms are known to be (from Table 5.4, page 91).

$$\text{S.S.}_{\text{about regression}} = C_{yy} - b_1 C_{y1} - b_2 C_{y2} - \ldots - b_p C_{yp} \qquad (7.33)$$
and
$$\text{S.S.}_{\text{total}} = C_{yy} \qquad (7.34)$$

7.3.10   Example. From Example 4.1.8, page 70, what is the coefficient of curvilinear correlation for the parabolic relationship between tensile strength and hardness of copper wire?

Solution: We want to calculate $R_{y \cdot 12}$, the coefficient of curvilinear correlation when $p = 2$. First we calculate the sum of squares about regression. From Example 4.1.6 we have

$$C_{yy} = 66,976,000$$

and from Example 4.1.8,
$$C_{y1} = 37,678$$
$$C_{y2} = 293,846$$
$$b_1 = 543.04$$
$$b_2 = 141.06$$

and from Eq. (7.33) we compute

$$\begin{aligned} \text{S.S.}_{\text{about regression}} &= C_{yy} - b_1 C_{y1} - b_2 C_{y2} \\ &= 66,976,000 - (543.04)(37,678) - (141.06)(293,846) \\ &= 5,060,221.20 \end{aligned}$$

From Example 4.1.6 we compute

$$\text{S.S.}_{\text{total}} = 66,976,000.00$$

Therefore, from Eq. (7.32),

$$R_{y \cdot 12} = \sqrt{1 - \frac{\text{S.S.}_{\text{about regression}}}{\text{S.S.}_{\text{total}}}}$$

$$= \sqrt{1 - \frac{5,060,221.2}{66,976,000}} = 0.96$$

the coefficient of curvilinear correlation.

7.3.11 Example. In Example 5.1.2, page 87, what is the coefficient of multiple correlation for the tensile strength of laminated plastic structural members on temperature and vacuum pressure?

Solution: From Example 5.1.4, page 91, we know from the ANOVA that

$$\text{S.S.}_{\text{about regression}} = 10,483,062.94$$
$$\text{S.S.}_{\text{total}} = 10,877,669.60$$

From Eq. (7.32),

$$R_{y \cdot 12} = \sqrt{1 - \frac{10,483,062.94}{10,877,669.60}}$$
$$= 0.19$$

the coefficient of multiple linear correlation.

7.4 Interpretation of Experimental Variance When the Levels of the Variables are Predetermined

In Sec. 7.3, we considered certain methods for interpreting the relationship between variables when the dependent variable, y, was always measured by a *single* random sample, $y_1, y_2, y_3, \ldots, y_n$. In such cases, any response, y_i, contains one basic source of measurement error, called *analytical error*. This analytical error can be illustrated as ε_i in the expression

$$y_i = \mu + \varepsilon_i \tag{7.35}$$

By summing both sides of Eq. (7.36) over all values of i, squaring, and solving for ε_i we are given

$$\sum_{i=1}^{n} \varepsilon_i^2 = \sum_{i=1}^{n} (y_i - \mu)^2 \tag{7.36}$$

and expressed in estimation parameters we get

$$\sum_{i=1}^{n} e_i^2 = \sum_{i=1}^{n} (y_i - \bar{y})^2 \tag{7.37}$$

as the sum of squares of the total variation in y. When no other sources of variation are partitioned, we therefore observe that

$$\text{S.S.}_{\text{total}} = \text{S.S.}_{\text{error}} = \sum_{i=1}^{n} (y_i - \bar{y})^2 \tag{7.38}$$

and only a single source of measurement error is involved.

The interpretation of the mean square estimates when column and row effects exist involves *two* basic measurement errors, namely, *analytical error* and *sampling error*. The mean squares, in such cases, represent unbiased estimates of such analytical and sampling effects.

When the levels of an independent random variable are predetermined, we then, in effect, take k samples of the dependent variable y with n_j responses per sample. For this situation we have as the mathematical model from Eq. (4.19), page 72,

$$y_{ij} = \mu + \tau_j + \varepsilon_{ij} \tag{7.39}$$

where τ_j is the column (and in this illustration, the sample) effect upon y_{ij}. From Eq. (4.29), page 77, the sum of squares for such a column (or sample) effect is given by

$$\text{S.S.}_{\text{columns}} = \sum_{j=1}^{k} \frac{y_{.j}^2}{n_j} - \frac{y_{..}^2}{N} = \text{S.S.}_{\text{samples}}$$

$$= \sum_{j=1}^{k} n_j (\bar{y}_{.j} - \bar{y}_{..})^2 \tag{7.40}$$

Knowing that

$$\bar{y}_{.j} = \sum_{i=1}^{n} y_{ij}/n_j \tag{7.41}$$

and

$$\bar{y}_{..} = \sum_{j=1}^{k} \sum_{i=1}^{n} y_{ij}/nk \tag{7.42}$$

we can rewrite Eq. (7.40) by substituting the universe effects from Eq. (7.39) for y_{ij} in Eqs. (7.41) and (7.42), thus:

$\text{S.S.}_{\text{samples}}$

$$= n_j \sum_{j=1}^{k} \left[\sum_{i=1}^{n} \frac{(\mu + \tau_j + \varepsilon_{ij})}{n_j} - \sum_{j=1}^{k} \sum_{i=1}^{n} \frac{(\mu + \tau_j + \varepsilon_{ij})}{n_j k} \right]^2$$

$$= n_j \sum_{j=1}^{k} \left[\left(\mu + \tau_j + \sum_{i=1}^{n_j} \varepsilon_{ij}/n_j \right) - \left(\mu + \sum_{j=1}^{k} \tau_j/k + \sum_{j=1}^{k} \sum_{i=1}^{n_j} \varepsilon_{ij}/n_j k \right) \right]^2$$

$$= n_j \sum_{j=1}^{n_j} \left[\tau_j - \left(\sum_{j=1}^{k} \tau_j/k \right) + \left(\sum_{i=1}^{n_j} \varepsilon_{ij}/n_j \right) + \left(\sum_{i=1}^{n_j} \sum_{j=1}^{k} \varepsilon_{ij}/n_j k \right) \right]^2$$

and on expanding the square

$$= n_j \sum_{j=1}^{k} \left[\tau_j - \left(\sum_{j=1}^{k} \tau_j/k \right) \right]^2 + \frac{n_j}{n_j^2} \sum_{j=1}^{k} \left[\sum_{i=1}^{n} \varepsilon_{ij} - \left(\sum_{i=1}^{n_j} \sum_{j=1}^{k} \varepsilon_{ij}/k \right) \right]^2$$

$$+ \text{cross products} \tag{7.43}$$

Knowing that $\qquad$ M.S. $= \text{S.S.}/\nu$

and then dividing Eq. (7.43) by $k - 1$, we get

$$\text{M.S.}_{\text{samples}} = \frac{n_j \sum_{j=1}^{k} \left[\tau_j - \left(\sum_{j=1}^{k} \tau_j/k \right) \right]^2}{k-1}$$

$$+ \frac{\frac{1}{n_j} \sum_{j=1}^{k} \left[\sum_{i=1}^{n} \varepsilon_{ij} - \left(\sum_{i=1}^{n_i} \sum_{j=1}^{k} \varepsilon_{ij}/k \right) \right]^2}{k-1} + \text{cross products} \quad \textbf{(7.44)}$$

To interpret the mean squares for samples we must determine what universe variance components are estimated by the expression in Eq. (7.44). To do this we must introduce a concept known as the *expected mean square*. This term can be better understood if we consider a few similar terms that are already familiar.

In Sec. 2.3, page 20, μ was described as the mean of a distribution. It can also be thought of as the expected or most likely value in a distribution. For a random variable x, we can write

$$E(x) = \mu$$

which says that the *expected value* (E) of x equals μ. Further, from Eq. (3.5), page 40, we can write the unbiased estimate for variance, $\hat{s}^2$, as

$$E(\hat{s}^2) = E\left[\frac{\sum_{i=1}^{n} (x - \bar{x})^2}{n-1} \right] = \sigma^2$$

giving that the expected value of $\hat{s}^2$ is σ^2.

In general, we can say that the expected value of the function $g(x)$ of the random variable x whose frequency function is $f(x)$ is given by

$$E[g(x)] = \int_{-\infty}^{\infty} g(x)f(x)\,dx \quad \textbf{(7.45)}$$

Also, when c is any constant, it follows from Eq. (7.45) that

$$E[cg(x)] = cE[g(x)]$$

and when the random variables x and y are in linear combination we are given that

$$E[g(x) + h(x)] = E[g(x)] + E[h(x)] \quad \textbf{(7.46)}$$

Returning to Eq. (7.44), we can now write this expression as an expected value utilizing the above rules

$$E(\text{M.S.}_{\text{samples}}) = n_j E \left\{ \frac{\sum_{j=1}^{k} \left[\tau_j - \left(\sum_{j=1}^{k} \tau_j/k \right) \right]^2}{k-1} \right\}$$

$$+ \frac{1}{n_j} \left\{ \frac{\sum_{j=1}^{k} \left[\sum_{i=1}^{n} \varepsilon_{ij} - \left(\sum_{i=1}^{n} \sum_{j=1}^{k} \varepsilon_{ij}/k \right) \right]}{k-1} \right\} \quad \textbf{(7.47)}$$

since the expected value of the cross products can be shown to be zero. Observing that the two terms on the right of Eq. (7.47) are both of the form

$$\hat{s}^2 = \frac{\sum_{i=1}^{n} (x - \bar{x})^2}{n - 1}$$

it follows that Eq. (7.47) can be rewritten thus:

$$E(\text{M.S.}_{\text{samples}}) = n_j \sigma_s^2 + \sigma_e^2$$

where σ_s^2 is the component of variance attributable to sampling error, and σ_e^2 is the component of variance attributed to analytical error when the independent variable is random. Therefore, the expected mean square (EMS) for the terms in the ANOVA Table 4.9, page 78, is given in Table 7.3.

Again, this EMS is only true when both the column and row variables are random. Variations in experimental design and conditions will produce variations in the EMS term. However, the fundamental concept is included here.

7.4.1   Test for Significance of Mean Squares. In Example 7.3.1 we tested the significance of regression by calculating the F ratio of the mean square "due to regression" to the mean square "about regression," Eq. (7.15), and tested the F number for significance. We have a similar test when we consider the mean squares for column effects and row effects in experiments. Suppose that we wish to test the hypothesis

$$H_0: \tau_j = 0 \tag{7.48}$$

against the alternate hypothesis

$$H_1: \tau_j > 0 \tag{7.49}$$

To make such a test we calculate the F ratio

$$F = \frac{(N - k)\left[\sum_{j=1}^{k} \dfrac{y_{.j}^2}{n} - \dfrac{y_{..}^2}{N}\right]}{(k - 1)\left[\sum_{i=1}^{n}\sum_{j=1}^{k} y_{ij}^2 - \sum_{j=1}^{k} \dfrac{y_{.j}^2}{n}\right]} = \frac{n\hat{s}_c^2 + \hat{s}_e^2}{\hat{s}_e^2} = 1 + \frac{n\hat{s}_c^2}{\hat{s}_e^2} \tag{7.50}$$

It can be seen that the test is essentially concerned with the ratio of the component of variance for columns, σ_c^2, to the component of variance for error, σ_e^2, *plus one*. A look at Appendix G for the distribution of F will confirm this. Note that the smallest critical F value is equal to 1.00.

7.4.2   Example. For Example 4.2.3, page 78, test column effect for significance at $\alpha = 0.05$.

TABLE 7.3
General ANOVA Table With EMS

Source	S.S.	ν	M.S.	E.M.S.
Columns	$\displaystyle\sum_{j=1}^{k} \frac{y_{.j}^2}{n_j} - \frac{y_{..}^2}{N}$	$k-1$	$\displaystyle\frac{\sum_{j=1}^{k} \dfrac{y_{.j}^2}{n_j} - \dfrac{y_{..}^2}{N}}{k-1}$	$n_j\sigma_c^2 + \sigma_e^2$
Error	$\displaystyle\sum_{i=1}^{n_i}\sum_{j=1}^{k} y_{ij}^2 - \sum_{j=1}^{k} \frac{y_{.j}^2}{n_j}$	$N-k$	$\displaystyle\frac{\sum_{i=1}^{n_i}\sum_{j=1}^{k} y_{ij}^2 - \sum_{j=1}^{k} \dfrac{y_{.j}^2}{n_j}}{N-k}$	σ_e^2
Total	$\displaystyle\sum_{i=1}^{n_i}\sum_{j=1}^{k} y_{ij}^2 - \frac{y_{..}^2}{N}$	$N-1$		

Similarly in Table 5.6 we see that the EMS for these effects are as shown in Table 7.4.

TABLE 7.4
General ANOVA Table with EMS

Source	S.S.	ν	M.S.	E.M.S.
Columns	$\displaystyle\sum_{j=1}^{k} \frac{y_{.jp}^2}{n_j} - \frac{y_{..p}^2}{N}$	$k - 1$	$\text{S.S.}_c/(k-1)$	$n\sigma_c^2 + \sigma_e^2$
Rows	$\displaystyle\sum_{i=1}^{n} \frac{y_{i.p}^2}{k} - \frac{y_{..p}^2}{N}$	$n - 1$	$\text{S.S.}_r/(n-1)$	$k\sigma_r^2 + \sigma_e^2$
Error	$\displaystyle\sum_{j=1}^{k}\sum_{i=1}^{n} y_{ijp}^2 - \sum_{j=1}^{k} \frac{y_{.jp}^2}{n} - \sum_{i=1}^{n} \frac{y_{i.p}^2}{k} + \frac{y_{..p}^2}{N}$	$N - k - n + 1$	$\text{S.S.}_e/(N - k - n + 1)$	σ_e^2
Total	$\displaystyle\sum_{j=1}^{k}\sum_{i=1}^{n} y_{ijp} - \frac{y_{..p}^2}{N}$	$N - 1$		

Solution: The hypothesis to be tested is

$$H_0: \tau = 0$$
$$H_1: \tau > 0$$

From Table 4.11, page 79, the F ratio is calculated as

$$F = \frac{\text{M.S.}_{\text{columns}}}{\text{M.S.}_{\text{error}}} = \frac{8.98}{2.77} = 3.24$$

With 3 and 16 degrees of freedom and $\alpha = 0.05$, the critical F number from Appendix G is 3.24. Therefore, H_0 is rejected and column effects are considered significant.

7.4.3 Example. In Example 4.2.5, test the hypothesis

$$H_0: \tau = 0$$

against the alternate hypothesis

$$H_1: \tau > 0$$

with an $\alpha = .01$.

Solution: From the ANOVA table for this problem (page 81) the F ratio is

$$F = \frac{\text{M.S.}_{\text{columns}}}{\text{M.S.}_{\text{error}}} = \frac{11.9}{11.2} = 1.06$$

With 3 and 16 degrees of freedom, $\alpha = .05$, the critical F number from Appendix G is 5.29. Since $5.29 > 1.06$, we accept $H_0: \tau = 0$. If a true difference between the power output of transformers exists, this study was not able to detect it.

7.4.4 Example. In Example 5.2.2, page 94, test the results in Table 5.9, page 96, to determine if speed and feed have a significant effect upon cutting tool life ($\alpha = 0.05$).

Solution: First, test the hypothesis that speed has no effect on tool life. That is,

$$H_0: \tau = 0$$
$$H_1: \tau > 0$$

From Table 5.9, the F ratio is

$$F = \frac{\text{M.S.}_{\text{columns}}}{\text{M.S.}_{\text{error}}} = \frac{9.4}{39.0} = 0.24$$

H_0 is obviously accepted ($F < 1.00$).
To test for feed effects,

$$H_0: v = 0$$
$$H_1: v > 0$$

From Table 5.9,

$$F = \frac{\text{M.S.}_{\text{rows}}}{\text{M.S.}_{\text{error}}} = \frac{50.8}{39.0} = 1.30$$

With 4 and 16 degrees of freedom and $\alpha = 0.05$, the critical F number from Appendix G is 3.01. Therefore, H_0 is accepted.

It can be concluded that if feed and speed has a real effect upon tool life, it could not be detected within the limits of this study.

7.4.5 Components of Variance. In Example 4.2.3, page 78, the resulting ANOVA table (Table 4.11) is repeated in Table 7.5, with the EMS column added.

TABLE 7.5

ANOVA Table for Example 4.2.3 with EMS

Source	S.S.	ν	M.S.	E.M.S.
Columns	26.95	3	8.98	$n\sigma_c^2 + \sigma_e^2$
Error	45.60	16	2.77	σ_e^2
Total	72.55	19		

From Table 7.5, we can write

$$E(\text{M.S.}) = n\sigma_c^2 + \sigma_e^2 \qquad (7.51)$$
$$\text{M.S.}_{\text{columns}} = n\hat{s}_c^2 + \hat{s}_e^2$$

and

$$\text{M.S.}_{\text{error}} = \hat{s}_e^2 \qquad (7.52)$$

where $\hat{s}_c^2$ and $\hat{s}_e^2$ are the unbiased estimates of σ_c^2 and σ_e^2, respectively. For the particular problem in Table 7.5,

$$\hat{s}_e^2 = \text{M.S.}_{\text{error}} = 2.77 \qquad (7.53)$$

an unbiased estimate of the error component of variance.

With $n = 5$, we can write

$$5\hat{s}_c^2 + \hat{s}_e^2 = \text{M.S.}_{\text{columns}} = 8.98$$

and

$$\hat{s}_c^2 = \frac{8.98 - 2.77}{5} = 1.24 \qquad (7.54)$$

an unbiased estimate of the component of variance attributable to column effects.

7.4.6   The Distribution of Variances. By knowing that the frequency function of a sum of squares is χ^2 distributed, Eq. (7.8), we can now determine the distribution of s^2. Given from Eq. (3.4) that

$$s^2 = (1/n) \sum_{i=1}^{n} (x_i - \bar{x})^2$$

$$= (1/n) \sum_{i=1}^{n} [(x_i - \mu) - (\bar{x} - \mu)]^2$$

$$= (1/n) \sum_{i=1}^{n} (x_i - \mu)^2 - (\bar{x} - \mu)^2 \qquad (7.55)$$

if we multiply by n/σ^2 we get

$$ns^2/\sigma^2 + \left(\frac{\bar{x} - \mu}{\sigma/\sqrt{n}}\right)^2 = \sum_{i=1}^{n} \left(\frac{x_i - \mu}{\sigma}\right)^2$$

If we take the moment generating function of both sides, we get

$$M_{\left[\frac{ns^2}{\sigma^2} + \left(\frac{\bar{x}-\mu}{\sigma/\sqrt{n}}\right)^2\right]}(\Theta) = M_{\Sigma\left(\frac{x_i-\mu}{\sigma}\right)^2}(\Theta) \qquad (7.56)$$

Given that s^2 and $\bar{x}$ are independently distributed (without proof), the left side of Eq. (7.56) can be rewritten

$$M_{\frac{ns^2}{\sigma^2}}(\Theta) M_{\left(\frac{\bar{x}-\mu}{\sigma/\sqrt{n}}\right)^2}(\Theta)$$

and Eq. (7.56) is expressed in terms of ns^2/σ^2 as

$$M_{\frac{ns^2}{\sigma^2}}(\Theta) = \frac{M_{\Sigma\left(\frac{\bar{x}-\mu}{\sigma}\right)^2}(\Theta)}{M_{\left(\frac{\bar{x}-\mu}{\sigma/\sqrt{n}}\right)^2}(\Theta)} \qquad (7.57)$$

Both of the functions on the right side of Eq. (7.57) are for a sum of squares of a normal variable with zero mean and unit variance. Hence, from Eq. (7.8), we rewrite Eq. (7.57) thus:

$$M_{\frac{ns^2}{\sigma^2}}(\Theta) = \frac{(1 - 2\Theta)^{-n/2}}{(1 - 2\Theta)^{-1/2}} = (1 - 2\Theta)^{-\frac{n-1}{2}} \qquad (7.58)$$

From Eq. (7.58) we can conclude that if x is normally distributed with variance σ^2, and s^2 is the sample variance based on a random sample of size n, then

$$\chi^2 = ns^2/\sigma^2 \qquad (7.59)$$

has a χ^2 distribution with $n - 1$ degrees of freedom.

From Eqs. (3.4) and (3.5), it is seen that

$$s^2 = \left(\frac{n-1}{n}\right)\hat{s}^2 \qquad (7.60)$$

By substituting Eq. (7.60) in Eq. (7.59), we have

$$\chi^2 = (n - 1)\hat{s}^2/\sigma^2 \tag{7.61}$$

as a form that expresses the distribution of $\hat{s}^2$, the unbiased estimate of σ^2.

7.4.7 Example. Suppose that in Example 4.2.3, page 78, we knew from past experiments that $\sigma_e^2 = 2.21$. We have computed $\hat{s}^2 = 2.77$. Suppose, too, that we wished to know if there has been any increase in the analytical or experimental error from past experiments. We wish, then, to test the hypothesis

$$
\begin{aligned}
H_0&: \sigma_e^2 = 2.21 \\
H_1&: \sigma_e^2 > 2.21 \\
\alpha &= .05
\end{aligned}
\tag{7.62}
$$

We test the hypothesis by calculating from Eq. (7.61)

$$\chi^2 = (n - 1)\hat{s}_e^2/\sigma_e^2 = 16(2.77)/2.21 = 20.05$$

To determine if this value is significant, we consult the table of the distribution of χ^2 in Appendix F. With sixteen degrees of freedom, we find that the table value is exceeded first by the above calculated value in the column headed by $p = 0.20$. For $\alpha = .05$ we therefore accept the hypothesis H_0, that $\sigma_e^2 = 2.21$. We can conclude, then, that if there has been a change in σ_e^2, this experiment was not able to detect it at the required confidence level.

7.4.8 Confidence Limits for Variances. Suppose that in Example 4.2.3 we wish to determine the limits within which the true value of σ_e^2 would be expected to fall with a given confidence. If, for instance, we wished to know between what two values, χ_1^2 and χ_2^2, that $(n - 1)\hat{s}_e^2/\sigma^2$ would fall 98 per cent of the time, we would determine the critical values from Appendix G. In Example 4.2.3 we can determine such confidence limits for σ_e^2. With sixteen degrees of freedom we find that the critical value for $p = 0.99$ is 5.812, and for $p = 0.01$ it is 32.000. The probability that $(n - 1)\hat{s}_e^2/\sigma_e^2 < 5.812$ is 0.01, and that $(n - 1)\hat{s}_e^2/\sigma_e^2 > 32.00$ is 0.01. Therefore

$$P(5.812 < (n - 1)\hat{s}_e^2/\sigma_e^2 < 32.000) = 0.98$$

The 98 per cent confidence limits for σ_e^2 can therefore be calculated from the inequality

$$\frac{(n - 1)\hat{s}_e^2}{5.812} < \sigma_e^2 < \frac{(n - 1)\hat{s}_e^2}{32.000} \tag{7.63}$$

or

$$\frac{16(2.77)}{5.812} < \sigma_e^2 < \frac{16(2.77)}{32.000}$$

reducing to
$$7.626 < \sigma_e^2 < 1.385$$
giving the confidence limits for σ_e^2.

7.5 Exercises   (Data sets are in Appendix D.)

7.1. Compute the regression equations of the following pairs from data set 3:
(a) y on x_1, (b) y on x_2, (c) y on $x_1 x_2$.

7.2. For the results in Exercise 7.1 set up ANOVA tables for the sources of
variation and test the appropriate hypotheses at $\alpha = 0.05$ for (a) y on x_1,
(b) y on x_2, (c) y on $x_1 x_2$.

7.3. For the results in Exercise 7.2 compute the correlation coefficients for the
following pairs and test for significance at $\alpha = 0.05$. (a) y and x_1, (b)
y and x_2, (c) y and $x_1 x_2$.

7.4. Observe the correlation coefficients in Exercise 7.3 and state your conclusions concerning the independent variables.

7.5. For data set 3, compute the multiple correlation coefficient for y as a
function of $x_1 x_2$.

7.6. Determine the limits between which the true variance will fall, with 95
per cent confidence, for Problem 7.2.

7.7. The standard deviation of the mileage for truck tires manufactured by a
certain company is 208.8 miles for a sample of nine tires. Find 95 per cent
confidence limits for the variance of all truck tires manufactured by the
company.

7.8. Filament current of vacuum tubes was measured from two different
production lines. A sample of thirteen from line number 1 had a standard
deviation of 1.3 micro amperes, while a sample of seven from line number
2 had a standard deviation of 3.2 micro amperes. Is there a difference
between these two production lines? State your hypothesis, and test at
$\alpha = 0.05$.

7.9. In Exercise 4.7, page 82, (a) test if the position of the cut parts from
blocks of RL-2405 plastic foam has a significant effect upon compression
yield strength $\alpha = 0.10$, (b) write the EMS column, and (c) calculate the
components of variance.

7.10. In Exercise 4.8, page 82, (a) test for significant effect between layers,
$\alpha = 0.05$, (b) write the EMS column, and (c) calculate the components of
variance.

7.11. In Exercise 5.7, page 97, (a) test for significant effects between columns
and between rows with $\alpha = 0.05$, (b) write the EMS column, and (c)
calculate the components of variance.

7.12. In Exercise 5.8, page 97, (a) test for significant effect of environment on
the ultimate tensile strength of adhesive with $\alpha = 0.01$.

CHAPTER 8

Interpretation of Means

In Chapter 7 we were concerned with the techniques associated with the interpretation of variance in experiments. In many cases where a test for variances produces a significant result, we are then logically concerned with the significant *levels* of a variable so that we may then concentrate analytical studies at these levels. For example, if we should find that the variable x has a significant effect on the variable y in Table 8.1,

TABLE 8.1

A General Experiment

	x	
x_1	x_2	x_3
y_{11}	y_{21}	y_{31}
y_{12}	y_{22}	y_{32}
y_{13}	y_{23}	y_{33}
	y_{24}	
$y_{1\cdot}$	$y_{2\cdot}$	$y_{3\cdot}$
n_1	n_2	n_3

we would probably be concerned with the question: Are all levels of x: x_1, x_2, and x_3, or only some levels, significantly different in their effects upon y? To ask the question another way: Given that the means of each level of x constitute best estimates of the mean of each variable, x_1, x_2, and x_3, are these sample means significantly different from each other?

8.1   Interpretation of a Sample Mean when σ Is Known

The interpretation of μ will usually be related to two types of concerns: (1) The test of hypothesis related to a change in μ, and (2) the determination of *confidence intervals* for predicting the expectation of μ. We will now consider each of these types of problems.

8.1.1   Test of Hypothesis Related to μ. Suppose that we wish to question if a given variable x has changed so that its mean, μ_0, is now equal to μ_1. We would therefore establish the hypothesis

$$H_0: \ \mu_0 = \mu_1$$
$$H_1: \ \mu_0 \neq \mu_1 \tag{8.1}$$
$$\alpha = .05$$

We can draw a sample of size n and compute the normal random variable z. We can then test its significance at an α risk of .05 by comparing the computed z to z_α (the critical value) in Appendix E. If the computed value exceeds the critical value, we can then reject H_0 and accept H_1 with 95 per cent confidence. If the calculated value z is less than z_α, H_0 is accepted for lack of sufficient confidence to reject it. When H_0 is accepted, the risk of a second kind (Sec. 6.4.1) is taken. The relationship between the α and β risks will be shown by an example.

8.1.2   Example. The mean tensile strength of a terminal wire embedded in potting compound of a class of capacitors is 6.0 psi with a standard deviation of 1.25 psi.

(a) A random sample of sixteen capacitors is taken after a slightly different potting compound is used. The mean of this sample was found to be 6.4 psi. With $\alpha = .05$, has a real increase in mean tensile strength occurred?

(b) What is the risk of saying that the true tensile strength is 6.0 psi when, in fact, it is 6.8 psi?

(c) Suppose that we wanted to design an experiment that would detect a real increase in tensile strength of 0.6 psi with an α risk of 0.05 and a β risk of 0.10. What size sample must we take?

(d) Draw the operating characteristic curve (Sec. 6.4.2) for the test in (c).

Solutions:

(a) The hypothesis to be tested is

$$H_0: \mu = 6.0$$
$$H_1: \mu > 6.0$$
$$\alpha = 0.05$$

This is called a *one-tail* test since it is only concerned with an *increase* in tensile strength and only the area under the normal curve on the upper end of the distribution is involved.

Calculate the normal variate

$$z = \frac{(\bar{x} - \mu)}{\sigma/\sqrt{n}} = \frac{(\bar{x} - \mu)\sqrt{n}}{\sigma}$$

$$= \frac{(6.4 - 6.0)\sqrt{16}}{1.25} = 1.28$$

From Appendix E, the critical value that excludes 5 per cent of the area on the upper end of the normal curve is 1.645. Since the calculated value is smaller, H_0 is accepted.

(b) When accepting H_0 in (a) we take the risk of a second kind (β). Following is a diagram of the problem:

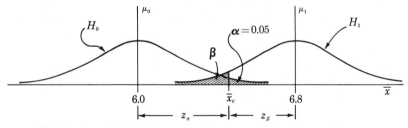

with the hypothesis being

$$H_0: \mu_0 = 6.0$$
$$H_1: \mu_1 = 6.8$$
$$\alpha = 0.05$$

First, we determine the value for $\bar{x}_c$, the critical point on the curve where H_0 is rejected if $\bar{x} > \bar{x}_c$ and accepted if $\bar{x} < \bar{x}_c$. Therefore, given the standard normal variate

$$z = \frac{\bar{x}_c - \mu_0}{\sigma/\sqrt{n}}$$

and solving for $\bar{x}_c$ we have

$$\bar{x}_c = \mu_0 + z\sigma/\sqrt{n}$$

Since $\bar{x}_c$ is the critical point for an α risk, we substitute z_α for z when $\alpha = 0.05$, and solve for

$$\bar{x}_c = \mu_0 + z_\alpha\sigma/\sqrt{n}$$
$$= 6.0 + 1.645(1.25)/\sqrt{16} = 6.514 \qquad (8.2)$$

We now want to determine the critical value for $\bar{x}_c$ in terms of H_1. We therefore compute

$$z_\beta = \frac{\mu_1 - \bar{x}_c}{\sigma/\sqrt{n}}$$

$$= \frac{6.8 - 6.514}{1.25/\sqrt{16}} = 0.915 \qquad (8.3)$$

From Appendix E, the β risk under the H_1 curve is therefore

$$P(z \leq -0.915) = 0.18$$

which is the risk of accepting H_0 when H_1 is true.

(c) In this problem we wish to determine the sample size required to detect a real increase in tensile strength of 0.6 psi with $\alpha = .05$ and $\beta = .10$. The hypothesis is

$$H_0: \mu_0 = 6.0$$
$$H_1: \mu_1 = 6.6$$

Since Eq. (8.2) and (8.3) have a common term, $\bar{x}_c$, we can set them equal

$$\mu_1 - z_\beta\sigma/\sqrt{n} = \mu_0 + z_\alpha\sigma/\sqrt{n}$$

and solve for n thus

$$\sigma/\sqrt{n} = \frac{\mu_1 - \mu_0}{z_\alpha + z_\beta}$$

$$n = \sigma^2 \frac{(z_\alpha + z_\beta)^2}{(\mu_1 - \mu_0)^2} \qquad (8.4)$$

For this problem, with $\alpha = 0.05$ the critical value (one tail) is $z_\alpha = 1.645$ and with $\beta = 0.10$, $z_\beta = 1.282$. By substituting in Eq. (8.4) we have

$$n = \frac{(1.25)^2(1.645 + 1.282)^2}{(6.6 - 6.0)^2}$$

$$= 37.2 \quad \text{or} \quad 38$$

giving that a sample of $n = 38$ must be drawn to detect a real increase in tensile strength of 0.6 psi with $\alpha = 0.05$ and $\beta = 0.10$.

(d) To construct the operating characteristic curve for (c), we first calculate the risks of a second kind that relate to a multiple of alternate hypotheses H_1. For example, let us assume the hypotheses

$$H_0: \mu_0 = 6.0$$
$$H_1: \mu_1 = 6.2$$
$$\mu_1 = 6.4$$
$$\mu_1 = 6.6$$
$$\mu_1 = 6.8$$

As in part (b), we calculate the critical value $\bar{x}_c$ from Eq. (8.2) thus

$$\bar{x}_c = \mu_0 + z_\alpha \sigma / \sqrt{n}$$
$$= 6.0 + 1.645(1.25)/\sqrt{38}$$
$$= 6.33$$

and calculate the successive probabilities for each alternate hypothesis in the following tabulation:

(1)	(2)	(3)	(4)
		$\dfrac{(2) \times \sqrt{n}}{\sigma}$	
μ_1	$[\bar{x}_c - (1)]$		$P[z \le (3)]^*$
6.0	$6.33 - 6.0 = \quad 0.33$	$(0.33\sqrt{38}/1.25) = \quad 1.63$	0.9484
6.2	$6.33 - 6.2 = \quad 0.13$	$(0.13\sqrt{38}/1.25) = \quad 0.64$	0.7389
6.4	$6.33 - 6.4 = -0.07$	$(-0.07\sqrt{38}/1.25) = -0.34$	0.3669
6.6	$6.33 - 6.6 = -0.27$	$(-0.27\sqrt{38}/1.25) = -1.33$	0.0918
6.8	$6.33 - 6.8 = -0.47$	$(-0.47\sqrt{38}/1.25) = -2.31$	0.0104

* From Appendix E.

The values in column (4) above represent the probability that the respective alternate hypothesis H_1 is true when H_0 is accepted. Or, it is the risk of accepting H_0 as true when the alternate hypothesis is actually true.

When such results are generalized for all possible alternate hypotheses, we have what is called an *operating characteristic curve*. Such a curve for this problem is shown in Fig. 8.1.

8.1.3   Confidence Limits for μ. Suppose that we have a case in which σ is known, and μ is unknown but can be estimated from the results of a sample. If we draw a random sample of size n and compute its mean $\bar{x}$, we can calculate

$$P(\bar{x} - z_\alpha \sigma / \sqrt{n} < \mu < \bar{x} + z_\alpha \sigma / \sqrt{n}) = 1 - \alpha \qquad \textbf{(8.5)}$$

where α is the risk of μ *not* falling within the *confidence limits*

$$\mu \pm z_\alpha \sigma / \sqrt{n} \qquad \textbf{(8.6)}$$

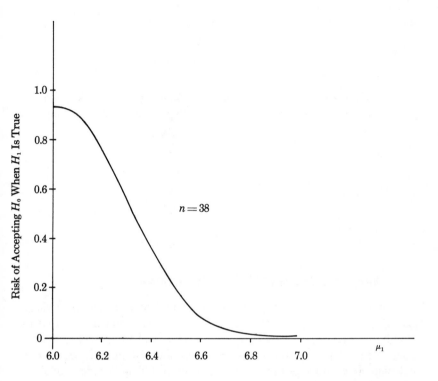

Fig. 8.1. The Operating Characteristic Curve for a One-Tail Test of the Hypothesis H_0: $\mu_0 = 6.0$, given $\sigma = 1.25$ and $\alpha = 0.05$ in Example 8.2.2

If we should be concerned with setting a limit in only one direction, Eq. (8.6) can be written

$$\mu + z_\alpha \sigma / \sqrt{n} \qquad (8.7)$$

which is the same as Eq. (8.2). In this case α would represent the risk of μ *exceeding* the confidence limit. The same can be done for a lower confidence limit. From Eq. (8.7) it follows that a confidence interval with only a lower limit considered would be written as

$$\mu - z_\alpha \sigma / \sqrt{n} \qquad (8.8)$$

with α being the risk of the true mean falling below the lower limit.

8.1.4 Example. Suppose that in Example 8.1.2 the true mean tensile strength μ_0 was unknown. Using the sample drawn in 8.1.2 (a), what would be the 95 per cent confidence limits within which μ_0 would be expected to fall?

Solution: Given from Example 8.1.2 (a),

$$\bar{x} = 6.4$$
$$n = 16$$
$$\sigma = 1.25$$

With $\alpha = 0.05$ for two-sided confidence limits from Appendix E, $z_\alpha = 1.96$. Therefore, from Eq. (8.6), 95 per cent confidence limits are

$$\mu \pm z_\alpha\sigma/\sqrt{n} = \bar{x} \pm z_\alpha\sigma/\sqrt{n}$$
$$= 6.4 \pm 1.96(1.25)/\sqrt{16}$$
$$= 6.4 \pm .61$$

The upper limit is

$$6.4 + .61 = 7.01$$

The lower limit is

$$6.4 - .61 = 5.79$$

8.2   Interpretation of μ When σ Is Unknown

Section 8.1 was concerned with experimental situations when sufficient past data is available or knowledge of the phenomenon exists so that the standard deviation, σ, of the distribution is known before an experiment is conducted. Quite often this knowledge does not exist and it is necessary to calculate an estimate of the standard deviation, $\hat{s}$, from a sample of size n. From such an estimate it is then possible to (1) test hypotheses concerning μ, and (2) set confidence intervals for μ. We already know that as $n \to \infty$ we can expect $\hat{s} \to \sigma$. In situations where n is large, we can consider $\hat{s} = \sigma$, and our analysis becomes identical to that in Sec. 8.1. In cases where $n \to 0$, $n > 1$, we cannot use the equation for z as in Eq. (8.23) since we would be measuring some variation in $\hat{s}$ that is attributable to the small size of n rather than as an unbiased estimate of σ. To overcome this error it is necessary to use the t distribution (Sec. 7.2) since it is a function of $\hat{s}$ rather than σ.

8.2.1   Example. The mean Rockwell hardness of a steel alloy is known to be 50.0. No past data was available to determine the standard deviation. Twenty specimens are taken at random. The results of the hardness tests on these specimens are shown in Table 8.2.

(a) From these results determine if a real change has occurred in the mean hardness ($\alpha = .05$).

(b) What are the 90 per cent confidence limits for the true hardness?

TABLE 8.2

Hardness Test Data for a Steel Alloy

Specimen Number	y Rockwell Hardness (c scale)	Specimen Number	y Rockwell Hardness (c scale)
1	49	11	52
2	57	12	48
3	54	13	54
4	51	14	56
5	48	15	51
6	53	16	55
7	52	17	50
8	55	18	50
9	59	19	50
10	51	20	52

Solutions:

(a) Calculate from the above data

$$n = 20 \qquad \sum x^2 = 54,882$$
$$\sum x = 1,046 \qquad \bar{x} = 52.3$$

Since σ is unknown, it must be estimated by the sample. Thus, from Eq. (3.6), we know that

$$\hat{s}^2 = [1/(n - 1)][\sum x^2 - (1/n)(\sum x)^2]$$
$$= (1/19)[54,882 - (1/20)(1,046)^2]$$
$$= 9.27$$

the unbiased estimate of σ^2. Using the t distribution

$$t = \frac{\bar{x} - \mu}{\hat{s}/\sqrt{n}}$$

Substituting data from the problem we test the hypothesis

$$H_0: \mu = 50.0$$
$$H_1: \mu \neq 50.0$$

thus

$$t = \frac{52.3 - 50.0}{\sqrt{9.27}/\sqrt{20}}$$
$$= 3.38$$

In Appendix H, for $\nu = 19$ the critical t value (two tail) is 2.093. Therefore, since $3.38 > 2.093$, the hypothesis H_0 is rejected and a real change in hardness of the steel alloy is assumed with 95 per cent confidence.

(b) When σ is not known and must be estimated by $\hat{s}$, Eq. (8.5) becomes

$$P(\bar{x} - t_\alpha \hat{s}/\sqrt{n} < \mu < \bar{x} + t_\alpha \hat{s}/\sqrt{n}) = 1 - \alpha \qquad (8.9)$$

which can be written as confidence limits

$$\mu \pm t_\alpha \mu/\sqrt{n} \qquad (8.10)$$

or when μ is unknown

$$\bar{x} \pm t_\alpha \hat{s}/\sqrt{n} \qquad (8.11)$$

From the above problem Eq. (8.11) becomes

$$52.3 \pm 1.729(\sqrt{9.27}/\sqrt{20}) = 52.3 \pm 2.53$$

giving the 90 per cent confidence limits for μ. The upper limit is

$$52.3 + 2.53 = 54.83$$

and the lower limit is

$$52.3 - 2.53 = 49.77$$

8.3 Difference Between Two Sample Means

To interpret the difference between sample means we must determine the distribution of such difference. Given that y_1 and y_2 are normally and independently distributed, then $y_1 - y_2$ is also normally distributed with mean

$$\mu_{y_1-y_2} = \mu_{y_1} - \mu_{y_2} \qquad (8.12)$$

and from Eq. (3.11), the variance of the differences is

$$\sigma^2_{y_1-y_2} = \frac{\sigma^2_{y_1}}{n_1} - \frac{\sigma^2_{y_2}}{n_2} \qquad (8.13)$$

8.3.1 When $\sigma^2_{y_1}$ and $\sigma^2_{y_2}$ Are Known. The distribution for the difference between two sample means when $\sigma^2_{y_1}$ and $\sigma^2_{y_2}$ are known is given by

$$z = \frac{\bar{y}_1 - \bar{y}_2}{\sqrt{\dfrac{\sigma^2_{y_1}}{n_1} + \dfrac{\sigma^2_{y_2}}{n_2}}} \qquad (8.14)$$

and the confidence limits are

$$(\bar{y}_1 - \bar{y}_2) \pm z_\alpha \sqrt{\frac{\sigma^2_{y_1}}{n_1} + \frac{\sigma^2_{y_2}}{n_2}} \qquad (8.15)$$

When $\sigma^2_{y_1}$ and $\sigma^2_{y_2}$ are equal, Eq. (8.14) becomes

$$z = \frac{\bar{y}_1 - \bar{y}_2}{\sigma_y \sqrt{\dfrac{1}{n_1} + \dfrac{1}{n_2}}} \qquad (8.16)$$

where $\sigma_y = \sigma_{y_1} = \sigma_{y_2}$, and Eq. (8.15) becomes

$$(\bar{y}_1 - \bar{y}_2) \pm z_\alpha \sigma_y \sqrt{\frac{1}{n_1} + \frac{1}{n_2}} \qquad (8.17)$$

When n_1 and n_2 are equal, Eq. (8.16) becomes

$$z = \frac{\bar{y}_1 - \bar{y}_2}{\sigma_y \sqrt{2/n}} \qquad (8.18)$$

where $n = n_1 = n_2$, and Eq. (8.17) becomes

$$(\bar{y}_1 - \bar{y}_2) \pm z_\alpha \sigma_y \sqrt{2/n} \qquad (8.19)$$

8.3.2   Example. A research laboratory developed a process for the extraction of chemically pure vanillin using a mixture of two commercially available solvents, Dupont "X" and Monsanto "Y." Nine random batches were run using a solvent mixture with 25 per cent Dupont "X" and 75 per cent Monsanto "Y." Another twelve random batches were run with a solvent mixture consisting of 75 per cent Dupont "X" and 25 per cent Monsanto "Y." The yield of vanillin was measured in pounds of vanillin (times 10) per gallon of waste.

The results are summarized in Table 8.3. The standard deviation for vanillin yield is known to be 2.70 lb/gal.

Test the results to determine if the mean yield of vanillin is determined by the type of solvent mixture.

Solution: This is a case where $\sigma_{y_1} = \sigma_{y_2}$ and is given as $\sigma_y = 2.70$ lb/gal. We wish to test the hypothesis

$$H_0: \mu_1 = \mu_2, \quad H_1: \mu_1 \neq \mu_2$$

where μ_1 and μ_2 are true means for the 25 per cent and 75 per cent mixtures, respectively. For $\alpha = .05$, Eq. (8.16) becomes

$$z = \frac{\bar{y}_1 - \bar{y}_2}{\sigma_y \sqrt{\dfrac{1}{n_1} + \dfrac{1}{n_2}}}$$

$$= \frac{26.6 - 25.5}{2.70 \sqrt{\dfrac{1}{9} + \dfrac{1}{12}}} = 2.09$$

and from Appendix E with $\alpha = .05$ (two tail), the critical value is

TABLE 8.3

Yield of Chemically Pure Vanillin in Pounds of Vanillin (Times 10) per Gallon of Waste for Example 8.3.2.

	Solvent Mixture (Per Cent of Dupont "X")	
	25%	75%
	23.7	26.5
	39.9	24.6
	24.6	22.2
	29.1	19.2
	27.6	25.4
	19.6	26.7
	27.7	29.7
	23.5	29.7
	23.4	24.1
		28.5
		26.4
		22.9
Total	239.1	305.9
n	9	12
Mean	26.6	25.5

1.96. We therefore reject H_0 and conclude that the yield of vanillin is significantly affected by the solvent mixture used.

8.3.3   When $\sigma_{y_1}^2$ and $\sigma_{y_2}^2$ Are Unknown. In many investigations values for $\sigma_{y_1}^2$ and $\sigma_{y_2}^2$ are not known and must be estimated from the sample parameters, $\hat{s}_{y_1}^2$ and $\hat{s}_{y_2}^2$, respectively. In such cases where the universe parameters are not known but are *assumed to be equal*, the variable

$$t = \frac{\bar{y}_1 - \bar{y}_2}{\hat{s}\sqrt{\dfrac{1}{n_1} + \dfrac{1}{n_2}}}$$

assumes the t distribution with

$$\hat{s} = \hat{s}_{y_1} = \hat{s}_{y_2} = \sqrt{\frac{\hat{s}_1^2(n_1 - 1) + \hat{s}_2^2(n_2 - 1)}{(n_1 + n_2 - 2)}} \qquad \textbf{(8.20)}$$

and $\nu = n_1 + n_2 - 2$. The confidence limits are

$$(\bar{y}_1 - \bar{y}_2) \pm t_\alpha \hat{s}\sqrt{1/n_1 + 1/n_2} \qquad \textbf{(8.21)}$$

8.3.4 Example. Suppose that in Example 8.3.2, the universe variance was not known. What are the 95 per cent confidence limits for vanillin yield if the standard deviations for true yield are (a) equal for each solvent mixture and (b) not equal?

Solution:

(a) Since $\sigma_{y_1}^2$ and $\sigma_{y_2}^2$ are not given we must estimate them from the sample data. For 25 per cent Dupont "X"

$$\sum y_1^2 = 6{,}623.38$$

and

$$\hat{s}_1^2 = \frac{\sum y_1^2 - \dfrac{(\sum y_1)^2}{n_1}}{n_1 - 1}$$

$$= \frac{6{,}623.38 - \dfrac{(239.1)^2}{9}}{8} = 33.91$$

For 75 per cent Dupont "X"

$$\sum y_2^2 = 7{,}905.55$$

$$\hat{s}_2^2 = \frac{7{,}905.55 - \dfrac{(305.9)^2}{12}}{11}$$

$$= 9.18$$

and since $\sigma_{y_1}^2$ and $\sigma_{y_2}^2$ are assumed to be equal we calculate from Eq. (8.20)

$$\hat{s} = \sqrt{\frac{\hat{s}_1^2(n_1 - 1) + \hat{s}_2^2(n_2 - 1)}{(n_1 + n_2 - 2)}}$$

$$= \sqrt{\frac{33.91(8) + 9.18(11)}{(9 + 12 - 2)}} = 4.43$$

From Eq. (8.21) confidence limits are

$$(\bar{y}_1 - \bar{y}_2) \pm t_\alpha \hat{s} \sqrt{1/n_1 + 1/n_2}$$

and substituting for 95 per cent limits

$$(26.6 - 25.5) \pm 2.093(4.43)\sqrt{1/9 + 1/12}$$
$$= 1.1 \pm 1.29$$

The upper limit is

$$1.1 + 1.29 = 2.39$$

and lower limit is

$$1.1 - 1.29 = 0 \text{ (no negative values)}$$

(b) If $\sigma_{y_1}^2$ and $\sigma_{y_2}^2$ cannot be assumed equal the confidence limits are

$$(\bar{y}_1 - \bar{y}_2) \pm t_\alpha \sqrt{\frac{\hat{s}_1^2}{n_1} + \frac{\hat{s}_2^2}{n_2}} \qquad (8.22)$$

with degrees of freedom determined by

$$\frac{1}{\nu} = \frac{1}{\nu_1}\left[\frac{\hat{s}_1^2/n_1}{\hat{s}_1^2/n_1 + \hat{s}_2^2/n_2}\right] + \frac{1}{\nu_2}\left[\frac{\hat{s}_2^2/n_2}{\hat{s}_1^2/n_1 + \hat{s}_2^2/n_2}\right] \qquad (8.23)$$

Therefore, from Eq. (8.23), the degrees of freedom in this problem are

$$\frac{1}{\nu} = \frac{1}{8}\left[\frac{33.91/9}{(33.91/9) + (9.18/12)}\right] + \frac{1}{11}\left[\frac{9.18/12}{(33.91/9) + (9.18/12)}\right]$$

$$\nu = 8.47 = 9$$

From Eq. (8.22) the 95 per cent confidence limits are

$$1.1 \pm 2.262 \sqrt{\frac{33.91}{9} + \frac{9.18}{12}}$$

$$= 1.1 \pm 4.82$$

with upper limit

$$1.1 + 4.82 = 5.92$$

and lower limit

$$1.1 - 4.82 = 0 \text{ (no negative values)}$$

Obviously, because of the small sample these limits are of very little value.

8.4   Difference Between Several Sample Means

In experiments where several levels of a variable have been predetermined, the y_{ij} responses are effectively grouped into several samples. In section 7.4.1 we used the F test to determine if certain sample effects were significant. In cases where such a test is significant the question then logically raised is, which of the means of k samples are significantly different? To answer this question we are usually concerned with comparison of more than two sample means (even though k can equal 2). The problem is an extension of Sec. 8.3 in which two sample means were compared.

8.4.1   Comparisons to be Made Determined Prior to Experimentation. The method of testing that is properly used depends upon the original objectives of the experiment. Often, the purpose of our investigation is to compare different levels of a variable with one particular level of concern (often called the "control"). When such is the case, we are able to determine the comparisons to be made between means *prior to experimentation*. The general confidence limits for such comparisons can be written as

$$(\bar{y}_c - \bar{y}_j) \pm t_\alpha \hat{s}\sqrt{2/n} \qquad (8.24)$$

being the same form as Eq. (8.21) with $n = n_1 = n_2$. To test the hypothesis

$$H_0: \mu_c = \mu_j$$
$$H_1: \mu_c \neq \mu_j \qquad (8.25)$$

we use the expression

$$t = \frac{\bar{y}_c - \bar{y}_j}{\hat{s}\sqrt{2/n}} \qquad (8.26)$$

for a given level of α. The value for $\hat{s}$ represents the estimate of σ_e, the standard deviation for error. In such analyses, then,

$$\hat{s} = \sqrt{\text{M.S.}_{\text{error}}}$$

and is calculated in the ANOVA.

8.4.2 Example. In Example 4.2.3 with data in Table 4.10, page 78, let us assume that column four was designated as the "control" prior to experimentation. Test the other columns to determine if their effect is significantly different from the "control" column effect. Use $\alpha = .05$.

Solution: From Table 4.11, the mean square for error is

$$\text{M.S.}_{\text{error}} = 2.77 = \hat{s}^2$$

The hypotheses to be tested are

$$H_0: \mu_1 = \mu_4$$
$$H_1: \mu_1 \neq \mu_4$$

and

$$H_0: \mu_2 = \mu_4$$
$$H_1: \mu_2 \neq \mu_4$$

and

$$H_0: \mu_3 = \mu_4$$
$$H_1: \mu_3 \neq \mu_4$$

Substituting in Eq. (8.26), we get for the first hypothesis

$$t = \frac{\bar{y}_c - \bar{y}_j}{\hat{s}\sqrt{2/n}}$$

$$= \frac{1.2 - 2.8}{\sqrt{(2.77)(2/5)}}$$

$$= -1.53$$

For the second hypothesis

$$t = \frac{1.2 - 2.2}{\sqrt{2.77(2/5)}}$$

$$= -0.95$$

and for the third hypothesis

$$t = \frac{1.2 - 4.4}{\sqrt{2.77(2/5)}}$$

$$= -3.04$$

For an $\alpha = .05$ and $\nu = 5 + 5 - 2 = 8$ the critical t value is 2.306. Therefore

$$\text{Accept: } H_0: \mu_1 = \mu_4$$
$$H_0: \mu_2 = \mu_4$$
$$H_1: \mu_3 \neq \mu_4$$

8.4.3 Comparisons Made After Experimentation. Another type of experimental situation can exist when there is no particular "control" level for a variable. In such cases we are not interested in any specific comparisons. We are interested in determining which particular levels of the variable are significantly different after it has been determined with an F test that the effects of the variable are generally significant. For k levels of a variable there would be $k(k - 1)/2$ possible paired comparisons that must be made. A risk of the first kind, α, would be taken for each of these paired comparisons giving a risk (α') of rejecting at least one hypothesis when it is true as

$$\alpha' = P(\text{risk of the first kind}) = \frac{k(k - 1)}{2} \alpha \qquad (8.27)$$

For example, in an experiment with $k = 4$ levels of a variable, the accumulated risk when all combinations of t tests are made at $\alpha = .05$ would be

$$\alpha' = \frac{k(k - 1)}{2} \alpha = \frac{(4)(3)}{2}(.05) = 0.30$$

which is obviously unsatisfactory.

If the investigator wishes to treat the experiment as an entity and require that all levels of the variable be compared with an $\alpha' = \alpha$ risk, then it is necessary that the critical value t_α be something larger, say t'_α, so that for any two means, $\bar{y}_i$ and $\bar{y}_j$, we are given that

$$t' = \frac{y_i - y_j}{\hat{s}/\sqrt{n}} \qquad (8.28)$$

is larger than the standard variable t. Confidence limits would therefore become

$$(y_i - y_j) \pm t'_\alpha \hat{s}/\sqrt{n} \qquad (8.29)$$

A satisfactory solution to this problem has only been determined in recent years. Methods have been developed by Tukey, Scheffe, and Duncan. **[9] [12] [18].**

8.5 Exercises

8.1. In an experiment relating to the accelerated lifetime of transistors manufactured by a particular company, it was found that one sample of 15 transistors had a mean lifetime of 253 hours and an s^2 of 49 hours. Another sample of 11 transistors had a mean lifetime of 285 hours and an s^2 of 36 hours. Can the difference in mean lifetime be attributed to chance? State your hypothesis. $\alpha = 0.10$.

8.2. The following data were collected while testing the accuracy of nonpolarized meters. By experience, we know the mean to be zero. A sample of five meters had a mean of 1.5 and a sample standard deviation of 1.2. Determine if a true difference has occurred. State your hypothesis. $\alpha = 0.05$.

8.3. Does a true difference in means exist between data set 1a and data set 1b at $\alpha = 0.10$?

8.4. What is the alpha level at which we can assume that the two samples below came from the same universe?

$$\bar{x}_1 = 3.111 \qquad \bar{x}_2 = 2.122$$
$$s_1 = 4 \qquad s_2 = 3$$
$$n_1 = 10 \qquad n_2 = 8$$

8.5. Make a test to determine if your coins were fair (a) in Exercise 3.1 and (b) in Exercise 3.2 page 52.

8.6. Test the difference between the means in Exercise 3.13. $\alpha = 0.10$.

8.7. Past experience indicates that the average total tube times for the problem in data set 1 is 1.50 minutes. From data in Exercise 3.9, (a) determine if a change in mean total tube times has occurred with 95 per cent confidence. (b) What is the risk of saying that the true mean total tube time is 1.50 minutes when in fact it is 1.60 minutes? (c) Suppose that we wanted to design an experiment that would detect a true difference in mean total tube time of 0.20 minutes with an α risk of 0.05 and a β risk of 0.05. What size sample should we take?

8.8. Draw the operating characteristic (O.C.) curve for Exercise 8.7.

8.9. Given that layer number 1 was the "control" for the experiment in data set 4, using the results from Exercise 4.8, what layers are significantly different from the "control"?

8.10. The A.C. noise in a D.C. signal was known to be 100 millivolts, peak to peak. How many data points would be required in a sampling operation to measure the true D.C. signal, μ, in volts within ± 10 millivolts with 95 per cent confidence, assuming that noise will not exceed 100 millivolts, 95 per cent of the time?

CHAPTER 9

Randomization in Experiments

The existence of *bias* is a very common problem that can often invalidate the results of an experiment. Any unmeasured, unknown, or undesirable influence upon the variation of the responses may contribute to erroneous conclusions related to a set of data. When such influences follow a specific pattern, they are referred to as bias in the data.

Such biased influences may be caused by uncontrolled differences in time, environment, procedure, etc. These biases can be removed from an experiment if they are recognized during the planning phase and proper measures are taken to control them. Often, however, it is difficult or impossible to recognize the many biases that can influence an experiment. More significantly, it is often impossible or undesirable to control such biases through specific design of experimental equipment. An alternative method of dealing with such bias is concerned with the procedure for gathering the data, called *randomization*.

An experiment is said to be randomized when the order in which the responses are taken has been predetermined in a way that each possible response is given an equal opportunity for occurrence. Such randomization can be accomplished in four basic ways:

(1) complete randomization,
(2) randomization with single-block restriction,
(3) randomization with dual-block restriction,
(4) randomization with multidual-block restriction.

9.1 The Nature of Bias

The nature of bias will be illustrated in two ways. First, suppose that we are testing a variable resistor at three different positions by conducting three different current levels through it. Voltage drop is measured as the response. Let us assume that as the resistor heats up, its resistance continuously changes but we are unaware of this constant change. Such a change is a biased influence upon the voltage drop of the resistor.

A second illustration is related to the common traditional method of conducting an experiment. The data for a 3 × 3 matrix experiment could be gathered by beginning in the upper left-hand corner, filling the cells in the first row from left to right, filling each row from top to bottom (the same way we read a page in a book). Now suppose that the given response was under a constant bias influence that varied with time, and a given response was measured at a constant increment of time, δt. If we indicate the constant amount of bias influence upon each response during a period of δt as b, the results in Table 9.1 are obtained.

TABLE 9.1

A 3 × 3 Matrix Experiment With b Units of Bias

	C_1	C_2	C_3
R_1	b	$2b$	$3b$
R_2	$4b$	$5b$	$6b$
R_3	$7b$	$8b$	$9b$

The R_1C_1 cell contains b units of bias and increases through the matrix from left to right, top to bottom, until the R_3C_3 cell contains $9b$ units of bias. Now suppose that the true effects of columns and rows are zero. The expected response in each cell would therefore be

$$y_{ij} = \mu + \varepsilon_{ij} \tag{9.1}$$

The existence of bias in each cell of Table 9.1 will thus produce the expected response

$$y_{ij} + \delta_{ij}b = \mu + \varepsilon_{ij} + \delta_{ij}b \tag{9.2}$$

where δ_{ij} is equal to the amount of bias influence in the ijth cell attributed to δt, assuming the values $1, 2, 3, \ldots, c \times r.$ (c = no. of columns, r = no. of rows.) The above method will therefore produce the responses shown in Table 9.2, indicating a successive bias in each response. Such a bias can

TABLE 9.2

Cell Responses for a Biased Experiment

	C_1	C_2	C_3
R_1	$\mu + \varepsilon_{ij} + b$	$\mu + \varepsilon_{ij} + 2b$	$\mu + \varepsilon_{ij} + 3b$
R_2	$\mu + \varepsilon_{ij} + 4b$	$\mu + \varepsilon_{ij} + 5b$	$\mu + \varepsilon_{ij} + 6b$
R_3	$\mu + \varepsilon_{ij} + 7b$	$\mu + \varepsilon_{ij} + 8b$	$\mu + \varepsilon_{ij} + 9b$

lead to erroneous conclusions by implying that a real row or column effect exists when it does not. To illustrate, it can be readily determined that the sum of the bias effects for R_1 is $6b$ ($b + 2b + 3b$), for R_2, it is $15b$, and for R_3, $24b$. With μ and ε_{ij} held constant we can plot the bias effect for rows as shown in Fig. 9.1.

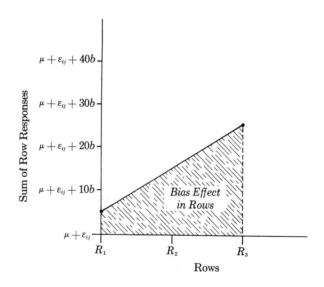

Fig. 9.1.   Illustration of Bias Effects

This bias influence could obviously be interpreted as row effects in this problem even though such real row effects have been assumed zero. Such misinterpretation can often be avoided by the control of the source of the bias through the proper design and planning of the experimental equipment. Often, however, this is not possible. Therefore, we randomize the bias effect so that it will be *neutralized* in the experiment.

The bias effect in this illustration can be tested for significance by running an analysis of variance on the coefficients for b and testing for row effects. Such an analysis produces the ANOVA in Table 9.3.

TABLE 9.3

ANOVA for Data in Table 9.2

Source	S.S.	ν	M.S.	F	Critical F
Columns	6.0	2	3.0	3.00	6.94
Rows	54.0	2	27.0	27.00*	6.94
Error	4.0	4	1.0		
Total	64.0	8			

* Highly significant

Note that the hypothesis, that no row effects exist, is erroneously rejected because of the existence of bias.

9.2 Complete Randomization

An experiment of a matrix form is said to be *completely randomized* when each cell response is given an equal opportunity to be run during the conduct of an experiment. In our 3×3 matrix example we wish to determine the cell order of experimentation in such a way that each remaining cell has an equal opportunity of becoming the next response. One way of doing this is to use a table of random numbers. Such a table is found in Appendix I, page 183. Our problem is to place the numbers 1 through 9 in the cells in such a way that the order in which the cells are filled with a response is randomly determined. The methods for doing this can vary. We will illustrate one approach.

Place the numbers 1 through 9 in the 3×3 matrix in any order as shown in Table 9.4.

Select any two rows of numbers from Appendix I. We will select the top two rows in this example (see Table 9.5). Observe the first (left-hand) number in the top row (which is a 2), and select the C_2R_1 cell in Table 9.4 since it contains the number 2. Now observe the first number in the second

TABLE 9.4
A 3 × 3 Matrix Experiment

	C_1	C_2	C_3
R_1	1	2	3
R_2	4	5	6
R_3	7	8	9

row (which is a 1) and place the number 1 in the C_2R_1 cell of the new 3 × 3 matrix shown in Table 9.6.

TABLE 9.5

Top Two Rows of Random Numbers from Appendix I

22 17 68 65 84	68 95 23 92 35	87 02 22 57 51	61 09 43 95 06	58 24 32 03 47
19 36 27 59 46	13 79 93 37 55	39 77 32 77 09	85 32 05 30 62	47 83 51 62 74

TABLE 9.6

A 3 × 3 Matrix Experiment

	C_1	C_2	C_3
R_1		1	
R_2			
R_3			

Repeat this process by observing the second number in the top row (a 2). We skip this number since it has already occurred once, and select the next number (a 1). We then select cell C_1R_1 from Table 9.4 (which contains the number 1). Now observe the second number in the second row (a 9) and place this number in the C_1R_1 cell in Table 9.7.

TABLE 9.7
A 3 × 3 Matrix Experiment

	C_1	C_2	C_3
R_1	9	1	
R_2			
R_3			

If we continue this process, using the rows of random numbers in Table 9.5, we will produce the random arrangement of the numbers 1 through 9 in Figure 9.8. This is one of 362,880 possible arrangements of the numbers 1 through 9 in a 3 × 3 matrix (a permutation of 9 things taken 9 at a time, or 9!).

TABLE 9.8

A Completely Randomized Experimental Plan

	C_1	C_2	C_3
R_1	9	1	8
R_2	5	7	6
R_3	3	2	4

A test of the randomness of Table 9.8 can be made by an analysis of variance. The ANOVA for such an analysis is shown in Table 9.9.

TABLE 9.9

ANOVA Table for Random Numbers in Table 9.8

Source	S.S.	ν	M.S.	F	Critical F
Between Col.	12.7	2	6.4	0.72	6.94
Between Rows	18.0	2	9.0	1.08*	6.94
Error	33.3	4	8.3		
Total	64.0	8			

* H_0 accepted @ $\alpha = 0.05$.

A comparison of the computed F numbers to the critical value (6.94) indicates that the hypotheses, that column and row effects equal zero, are accepted. The calculated F numbers are also quite near the expected true value 1.00 when no column or row effects exist.

Any matrix that has been completely randomized should meet this test. The matrix in Table 9.8 represents the experimental plan. We will make our first measurement with the column variable at the C_2 level and the row variable at the R_1 level, placing the response value in cell C_2R_1. Our second measurement will be taken at the C_2 level and R_3 level with the response placed in the C_2R_3 cell. This procedure is followed until the C_1R_1 cell is filled last, since it contains the ninth response measurement. With the experiment conducted in this way, any bias has been neutralized throughout all measurements. The experiment has been completely randomized.

9.3   Single-Block Randomization

Suppose that in a 3×3 experiment we restrict the randomizing process within columns or within rows. In other words, when columns are block randomized we completely randomize the measurements within each column. If rows are block randomized, we completely randomize the measurements within each row. For example, suppose that we choose the columns in a 3×3 matrix to be block randomized. We would, therefore, make a random selection of each cell order, one block at a time. We would first determine the random ordering of cells C_1R_1, C_1R_2, and C_1R_3, giving us a randomized block in column C_1. We would repeat this procedure in C_2 and C_3 and produce the experimental plan in Table 9.10.

TABLE 9.10

A Randomized-Block Experimental Plan

	C_1	C_2	C_3
R_1	1	1	2
R_2	2	3	3
R_3	3	2	1

The same procedure could obviously be followed for rows as well as columns, and for any number of rows or columns. An arrangement as in Table 9.10 is an experimental plan commonly referred to as a *randomized block design*.

9.4   Dual-Block Randomization

If we restrict the randomization in blocks both in the columns and the rows, we produce a *double randomized* block experiment. To do this requires that the random selections be made in each cell, making certain that no value repeats itself in any column or row. Table 9.11 illustrates such a design.

If we substitute a, b, and c for 1, 2, and 3 and consider these to be levels of a third variable, we develop a design known as a *Latin-Square experiment*. A 3×3 Latin-Square is shown in Table 9.12. Such a design

TABLE 9.11

A Double Randomized-Block Experiment Plan

	C_1	C_2	C_3
R_1	2	3	1
R_2	1	2	3
R_3	3	1	2

can be produced for any number of columns and rows, but the number of each must be equal (a square).

TABLE 9.12

A 3 × 3 Latin-Square Experimental Plan

	C_1	C_2	C_3
R_1	b	c	a
R_2	a	b	c
R_3	c	a	b

The analysis of variance for such a design is similar to a two-variable situation.

9.4.1 Example. In Example 5.2.3 there were five different tool steel alloys used. Table 9.13 is reproduced below with alloys A through E randomly placed in the cells with dual-block restriction. Analyze this Latin Square experiment to determine if tool steel alloy has a significant effect upon tool life.

Solution: From Example 5.2.3,

$$S.S._{total} = 864.0$$
$$S.S._{speed} = 37.6$$
$$S.S._{feed} = 203.2$$

and from Table 9.13,

$$S.S._{alloy} = \frac{(93)^2 + (98)^2 + (112)^2 + (112)^2 + (90)^2}{5} - \frac{(505)^2}{25}$$

$$= 10,288.2 - 10,201.0 = 87.2$$
$$S.S._{error} = 864 - 37.6 - 203.2 - 87.2 = 536.0$$

TABLE 9.13

Tool Life, in Hours, for Various Speeds, Feeds, and Tool Steel Alloys

	Speed					
In./Rev. \ r.p.m.	100	120	140	160	180	Total
0.005	A 16	B 22	E 24	D 29	C 28	119
0.010	D 24	E 18	C 23	B 23	A 25	113
0.015	C 11	D 27	B 10	A 13	E 18	79
0.020	B 29	C 21	A 18	E 14	D 11	93
0.025	E 16	A 21	D 21	C 29	B 14	101
Total	96	109	96	108	96	505

(Feed is the row variable label)

Tool Steel Alloy (Totals)					
A	B	C	D	E	Total
93	98	112	112	90	505

ANOVA Table:

Source	S.S.	ν	M.S.	F
Speed	37.6	4	9.4	
Feed	203.2	4	50.8	
Alloy	87.2	4	21.8	0.49*
Error	536.0	12	44.7	
Totals	864.0	24		

* Obviously not significant.

9.5 Multidual-Block Randomization

A still further restriction on randomization in experiments is possible by superimposing one Dual-Block (or Latin-Square) experiment on another. For example, suppose that we superimpose another Latin-Square design on the design in Table 9.12. Such an arrangement is illustrated in Fig. 9.2.

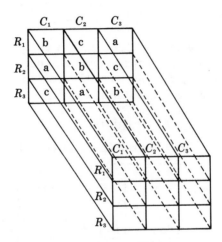

Fig. 9.2. Two Experimental Designs Superimposed

Our randomizing task is to select the levels of a fourth variable, α, β, and γ, for the front matrix in such a way that no pairing with the rear matrix will be repeated in a cell. For example, if a random selection places β in the C_1R_1 cell of the front matrix, we form the pairing βb, with the rear matrix. Then our restriction would not allow β to be entered in either the C_2R_2 cell or C_3R_3 cell since a duplication of the βb pairing would result. An example of a multidual-block design is shown in Table 9.14.

In none of the cells is the pairing of the Greek and Arabic letters repeated. Such a design is known as a *Graeco-Latin Square*. It may contain any number of columns or rows, but the number of columns must equal the number of rows.

TABLE 9.14

A Multidual-Block Experimental Plan

	C_1	C_2	C_3
R_1	γa	βb	αc
R_2	βc	αa	γb
R_3	αb	γc	βa

9.5.1   Example. If in Example 9.4.1 we now consider that each of the five different tool steel alloys were subjected to one each of five different heat treatments, α, β, γ, δ, ε, our data table would appear as in Table 9.15. Does heat treatment significantly affect tool life?

TABLE 9.15

Tool Life Data for Example 9.5.1

Feed \ Speed	100	120	140	160	180	Total
0.005	$A\alpha$ 16	$B\beta$ 22	$E\varepsilon$ 24	$D\delta$ 29	$C\gamma$ 28	119
0.010	$D\beta$ 24	$E\gamma$ 18	$C\alpha$ 23	$B\varepsilon$ 23	$A\delta$ 25	113
0.015	$C\varepsilon$ 11	$D\alpha$ 27	$B\delta$ 10	$A\gamma$ 13	$E\beta$ 18	79
0.020	$B\gamma$ 29	$C\delta$ 21	$A\beta$ 18	$E\alpha$ 14	$D\varepsilon$ 11	93
0.025	$E\delta$ 16	$A\varepsilon$ 21	$D\gamma$ 21	$C\beta$ 29	$B\alpha$ 14	101
Total	96	109	96	108	96	505

Solution: The only additional computation needed in this case is the sum of squares due to the Greek letters, i.e., heat treatment and a new error sum of squares.

This will now be computed.

Heat Treatment	Total	(Total)^2
α	94	8,836
β	111	12,321
γ	109	11,881
δ	101	10,201
ε	90	8,100
	505	51,339

Heat treatment sum of squares $= \dfrac{51,339}{5} - 10,201$

$$= 66.8$$

From data in Example 9.4.1:
Error sum of squares $= 864 - 37.6 - 203.2 - 87.2 - 66.8$
$$= 469.2$$

ANOVA Table:

Source	Sum of Squares	ν	M.S.	F
Columns	37.6	4	9.4	
Rows	203.2	4	50.8	
Alloys	87.2	4	21.8	
Heat treatment	66.8	4	16.7	.28*
Error	469.2	8	58.6	
Totals	864.0	24		

* Not significant.

There is theoretically no limit on the number of Latin-Square matrices that can be superimposed in this manner. Practically speaking, however, the problem of meeting all the restrictions on randomization in such a design becomes extremely complex with the addition of other matrices.

9.6 Exercises

9.1. In a 4 × 4 experiment, what is the number of ways in which a row or column can be randomized?

9.2. Given the following 4 × 4 experiment, completely randomized, conduct a test of randomness by an analysis of variance.

	C_1	C_2	C_3	C_4
R_1	8	7	14	16
R_2	6	15	13	9
R_3	5	3	4	2
R_4	10	12	1	11

9.3. Design a 4×4 experiment and (a) completely randomize, (b) block randomize by row, (c) dual-block randomize, (d) multidual-block randomize.

9.4. For what purpose are experiments randomized? If randomization in an experiment is not possible, what other alternatives are available to control bias?

APPENDIX A

Combinatorial Analysis

If E_1 can occur in n_1 ways and E_2 can occur in n_2 ways, then, E_1E_2 can occur n_1n_2 ways. For example,

Let:

$E_1 = $ office of president

$E_2 = $ office of vice-president

$n_1 = $ five candidates for president

$n_2 = $ three candidates for vice-president

Therefore:

$$E_1E_2 \text{ can occur } n_1n_2 \text{ or } 3 \times 5 = 15 \text{ ways.}$$

In many applications of probability the problem of counting the number of sample points corresponding to the occurrence of a particular event can often become quite complex. Such sample points can be selected from a particular set in two basic arrangements, one called a *permutation* and the other called a *combination*.

A permutation is an arrangement of objects in which the relative *position* of the objects to one another is considered. A combination is an arrangement in which position is not considered.

In the case of a coin, we know that the event (heads) can occur only once in a single toss. Such a basic arrangement could be thought of as a permutation of one event taken one at a time. Since only one position exists, the arrangement can also be described as a combination of one event taken one at a time.

If we have three letters, a, b, c, and take them two at a time and place them into all possible arrangements with position or order considered, we get ab, ac, ba, bc, ca, cb. Therefore, three letters arranged two at a time give six permutations. If position or order is not considered, we find from this example that the arrangements ab and ba are the same. This is also true for ac, ca and bc, cb. Therefore, we can say that three letters arranged two at a time yields three combinations, ab, ac, bc.

To generalize this, we take n letters and arrange r of them in r different positions giving us a permutation of n letters taken r at a time. Starting with the first letter position, any one of the n letters may be chosen for this position. After the first position has been filled, there are $n - 1$ letters that can be placed in the second position, $n - 2$ letters for the third position, and, finally, $n - r + 1$ letters for the rth position. Hence the total number of choices for the first two positions would be $n(n - 1)$, for the first three positions would be $n(n - 1)(n - 2)$, and for r positions $n(n - 1)(n - 2) \ldots (n - r + 1)$. The permutation of n things taken r at a time can then be stated as

$$_nP_r = n(n - 1)(n - 2) \ldots (n - r + 1) \qquad \textbf{(A.1)}$$

and for $r = n$, Eq. (A.1) becomes

$$_nP_n = n(n - 1)(n - 2) \ldots (n - n + 1) = n! \qquad \textbf{(A.2)}$$

and, in factorial terms, the permutation of n things taken r at a time is

$$_nP_r = \frac{n(n - 1)(n - 2) \ldots (1)}{(n - r)(n - r - 1) \ldots (1)} = \frac{n!}{(n - r)!} \qquad \textbf{(A.3)}$$

when, by definition, $0! = 1$.

In the case of the coin, we have $n = 1$ and $r = 1$, therefore, from Eq. (A.3)

$$_nP_r = \frac{n!}{(n - r)!} = \frac{1}{(1 - 1)!} = 1$$

For three letters, a, b, c, taken two at a time, we have $n = 3$ and $r = 2$. Therefore,

$$_nP_r = \frac{n!}{(n - r)!} = \frac{3 \cdot 2 \cdot 1}{(3 - 2)!} = \frac{6}{1} = 6$$

This particular permutation could also be thought of as an arrangement of all possible combinations, ab, ac, ba, bc, cb, ca. From Eq. (A.2) we can deduce that there are $r!$ number of arrangements of r objects in r positions.

Hence, if we denote the combination of n things taken r at a time by the symbol $\binom{n}{r}$, we can write

$$_nP_r = \binom{n}{r} r!$$

giving

$$\binom{n}{r} = \frac{_nP_r}{r!} = \frac{n!}{r!(n-r)!} \qquad (A.4)$$

Formula (A.4) is the combination of n things taken r at a time.

In the case of the coin where $n = 1$ and $r = 1$, we get from Formula (A.4)

$$\binom{n}{r} = \frac{n!}{r!(n-r)!} = \frac{1}{1(1-1)!} = \frac{1}{1 \cdot 1} = 1$$

the number of combinations.

In the case of the three letters, $n = 3$ and $r = 2$, we get from Formula (A.4)

$$\binom{n}{r} = \frac{n!}{r!(n-r)!} = \frac{3 \cdot 2 \cdot 1}{2 \cdot 1(1)} = 3$$

the number of different combinations.

APPENDIX B

Special Frequency Functions

B.1 Distribution Functions

In the case of three coins if we wished to calculate the probability of getting $x \leq 2$, we could calculate the probability of getting no heads, $1/8$, the probability of getting one head, $3/8$, and add them to the probability of getting two heads, $3/8$, giving $1/8 + 3/8 + 3/8 = 7/8$, the probability of getting two heads or less ($x \leq 2$).

This calculation is the summation of all values of the discrete random variable (x) that were less than or equal to the specified value. This function can be written

$$F(x) = \sum_{t \leq x} f(t) \tag{B.1}$$

and is known as the *distribution function* $F(x)$ for a discrete variable x. The frequency function $f(x)$ gives the probability of getting a particular value of x. The distribution function $F(x)$ gives the probability that a particular value of x will be less than or equal to that value. A graph of $F(x)$ for the toss of three coins is shown in Fig. B.1.

It can be seen, for example, that $F(x)$ for $x = 2$ is $7/8$ since

$$F(x) = \sum_{t \leq x} f(t) = 1/8 + 3/8 + 3/8 = 7/8$$

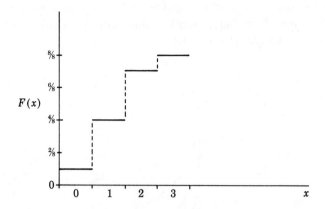

Fig. B.1. Graph of the Distribution Function F(x) for the Toss of Three Coins

The distribution function $F(x)$ for the continuous random variable x is defined by

$$F(x) = \int_{-\infty}^{x} f(t)\, dt \tag{B.2}$$

B.2 Joint Continuous Frequency Functions

The frequency function for two variables x and y is denoted by $f(x, y)$ and is three dimensional. A frequency function for n continuous random variables $x_1, x_2, \ldots, x_n$ is a function $f(x_1, x_2, \ldots, x_n)$ that possesses the following properties:

$$f(x_1, x_2, \ldots, x_n) \geq 0 \tag{B.3}$$

$$\int_{-\infty}^{\infty} \cdots \int_{-\infty}^{\infty} f(x_1, x_2, \ldots, x_n)\, dx_1\, dx_2 \ldots dx_n = 1 \tag{B.4}$$

$$\int_{a_n}^{b_n} \cdots \int_{a_1}^{b_1} f(x_1, x_2, \ldots, x_n)\, dx_1\, dx_2 \ldots dx_n$$

$$= P\{a_1 < x_1 < b_1, \ldots, a_n < x_n < b_n\} \tag{B.5}$$

B.2.1 Example. The graph of the function $f(x, y) = e^{-(x+y)}$ is shown in Fig. B.2. When $f(x, y)$ is defined to be zero for negative values of x and y, Eqs. (B.3) and (B.4) above are satisfied. In this example, from Eq. (B.4) we get

$$P\{1 < x < 2,\ 0 < y < 2\} =$$
$$\int_0^2 \int_1^2 e^y\, dx\, dy\, (e^{-1} - e^{-2})(e^0 - e^{-2}) = 0.20$$

and is represented as a volume in Fig. B.2. This *joint frequency function* is the function of two independent random variables whose functions are $f_1(x_1) = e^{-x_1}$, and $f_2(x_2) = e^{-x_2}$ [20].

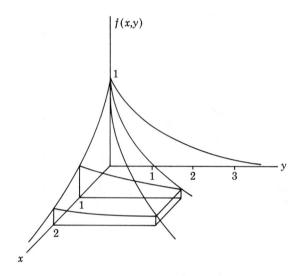

Fig. B.2.   Graph of the Function $f(x,y) = e^{-(x+y)}$

APPENDIX C

Interpretation of Frequency Data

In some areas of application the dependent variable is not of the continuous type as assumed in the main body of this book. Often it is desirable to measure responses that occur as frequencies, such as, the number of times an event has occurred. These data will occur as integers. The analysis and interpretation of such data will be discussed.

Suppose that in Example 4.2.5, the open circuit test on four different transformers, we recorded the number of times the transformer exceeded 182 watts of power output in the five observations. Inspection of Table 4.12, page 80, will give these results.

From past experience, it is known that the probability that a response will exceed 182 watts is $p = .44$. Therefore, from Eq. (7.1) we have

$$\chi^2 = \frac{(m - pn)^2}{pn} \tag{C.1}$$

the distribution of the differences between observed and expected frequencies. Table C.1 shows the calculations necessary to compute

$$\chi^2 = \frac{9.27}{8.8} = 1.05 \tag{C.2}$$

167

To test the hypothesis

$$H_0: \ p = .44$$
$$H_1: \ p \neq .44$$

(C.3)

the critical value from Appendix F, with $\nu = 3$ and $\alpha = .10$, is 6.25. The hypothesis that $p = .44$ is therefore accepted.

TABLE C.1

Computation for Frequency Data

Transformer Number	A	B	C	D	Total
(a) Number (m) Exceeding 182 watts	2	3	1	5	11
(b) Probability of Exceeding (p)	0.44	0.44	0.44	0.44	0.44
(c) Number of Observations (n)	5	5	5	5	20
(d) Number Expected to Exceed, (b) $\times$ (c)	2.2	2.2	2.2	2.2	8.8
(e) Deviation, (a) $-$ (d)	-0.2	0.8	-1.2	2.8	2.2
(f) (e)^2	0.04	0.16	1.44	7.63	9.27

A two-way table of frequency data is called a *Contingency Table* [9]. The analysis of such data is similar to the illustration above.

Other analyses of frequency data relate to the binomial distribution. It was illustrated in Example 2.4.2 that the calculation of the binomial distribution becomes very laborious as n increases. If n is large, the variable

$$z = \frac{m - np}{\sqrt{npq}}$$

(C.4)

is approximately normally distributed. The approximation is good if $np > 5$ when $p < 1/2$, and $nq > 5$ when $p > 1/2$ [20]. As a proportion, Eq. (C.4) can be written

$$z = \frac{m/n - p}{\sqrt{\dfrac{pq}{n}}}$$

(C.5)

where

$$\mu_{m/n} = p$$

(C.6)

and

$$\sigma_{m/n} = \sqrt{\frac{pq}{n}}$$

(C.7)

the standard error of a proportion.

Similarly to the above, when m_1 and m_2 occurrences of an event are observed for n_1 and n_2 trials, respectively, the variable

$$z = \frac{m_1/n_1 - m_2/n_2}{\sqrt{\dfrac{p_1q_1}{n_1} + \dfrac{p_2q_2}{n_2}}} \qquad \text{(C.8)}$$

is approximately normally distributed with

$$\mu_{m_1/n_1 - m_2/n_2} = p_1 - p_2 \qquad \text{(C.9)}$$

and

$$\sigma_{m_1/n_1 - m_2/n_2} = \sqrt{\frac{p_1q_1}{n_1} + \frac{p_2q_2}{n_2}} \qquad \text{(C.10)}$$

the standard error of the difference between proportions. This approximation is good when each n_ip_i exceeds 5 as $p_i < 1/2$ and n_iq_i exceeds 5 as $p_i > 1/2$.

When p_1 and p_2 are unknown and are estimated from the samples, the variable

$$t = \frac{m_1/n_1 - m_2/n_2}{s^2_{m/n}\sqrt{1/n_1 + 1/n_2}} \qquad \text{(C.11)}$$

is t distributed with

$$s^2_{m/n} = \frac{\left(\dfrac{m_1 + m_2}{n_1 + n_2}\right)\left(1 - \dfrac{m_1 + m_2}{n_1 + n_2}\right)}{n_1 + n_2} \qquad \text{(C.12)}$$

being the estimate of the variance of the proportion, m/n, where $m = m_1 + m_2$ and $n = n_1 + n_2$.

Consider an example. Suppose that from past experience we know the probability of getting a defective part is $p = 0.4$. If from a lot of 100 parts we found 53 to be defective, what can we say about the lot coming from past production?

To solve this problem we first establish the hypothesis that for the new lot

$$H_0: \ p = 0.4$$
$$H_1: \ p \neq 0.4$$

with $\alpha = 0.05$. We then calculate

$$m/n = 53/100 = .53$$

and since $np = (100)(0.4) = 40 > 5$ and $p < 1/2$ we use (C.5) thus,

$$z = \frac{m/n - p}{\sqrt{\dfrac{pq}{n}}} = \frac{0.53 - .4}{\sqrt{\dfrac{(0.4)(0.6)}{100}}} = 2.65$$

For $\alpha = 0.05$, two-tail test, the critical z value is 1.96. Therefore H_0 is rejected. We can therefore conclude that the lot did not come from past production.

APPENDIX D

Data Sets for Exercises

DATA SET 1

An experiment was conducted to determine the time required to place electron tubes in their receptacles. Participants were requested to place five varying types of electron tubes into their respective receptacles, where both the electron tubes and the receptacles were color coded. The time required for placing the first tube in its correct receptacle, together with the time required for placing all five tubes in their respective receptacles was recorded. Random selection of tube placement was employed.

170

a. First Tube Times (Minutes)

0.12	0.31	0.04	0.06	0.06	0.04	0.35	0.11	0.04
0.12	0.17	0.11	0.03	0.96	0.26	0.10	0.14	0.03
0.85	0.29	0.32	0.04	0.12	0.17	0.28	0.05	0.03
0.13	0.26	0.12	0.05	0.08	0.07	0.38	0.07	0.15
0.18	0.37	0.06	0.28	0.10	0.07	0.29	0.35	0.04
0.20	0.75	0.12	0.09	0.14	0.08	0.13	0.21	0.05
0.56	0.20	0.07	0.36	0.04	0.33	0.21	0.11	0.03
0.16	0.76	0.10	0.13	0.35	0.27	0.13	0.04	0.23
0.04	0.19	0.14	0.19	0.08	0.04	0.15	0.08	0.11
0.13	0.11	0.52	0.10	0.07	0.14	0.10	0.54	0.14
0.08	0.21	0.04	0.04	0.12	0.21	0.42	0.04	0.09
0.04	0.06	0.15	0.05	0.15	0.05	0.14	0.09	0.11
0.21	0.80	0.19	0.03	0.50	0.04	0.12	0.08	0.06
0.11	0.06	0.06	0.04	0.14	0.26	0.05	0.14	0.11
0.35	0.20	0.07	0.04	0.08	0.11	0.30	0.08	
0.80	0.08	0.08	0.05	0.09	0.18	0.30	0.04	
0.10	0.09	0.06	0.22	0.09	0.38	0.10	0.03	
0.04	0.04	0.07	0.05	0.35	0.11	0.09	0.02	

b. Total Tube Times (Minutes)

0.81	2.14	1.10	2.99	1.00	2.37	0.46	1.26
0.54	1.74	0.98	0.40	0.52	1.61	1.31	0.59
1.73	2.08	0.56	0.36	1.87	0.60	0.80	0.42
0.43	0.95	1.07	0.30	0.43	0.90	1.22	1.12
0.98	2.36	1.28	0.54	0.80	1.14	1.01	0.51
0.98	1.42	0.72	0.28	1.16	1.15	0.69	1.01
1.53	0.74	0.76	0.48	0.48	2.55	0.58	0.63
0.32	0.75	0.96	0.64	1.42	0.51	0.40	1.48
0.91	0.40	0.87	0.94	0.86	1.02	0.55	1.41
0.43	2.69	0.58	0.65	0.55	0.92	2.37	0.56
0.93	1.02	0.36	1.31	1.07	0.72	0.62	0.87
0.86	0.63	0.62	1.68	0.60	0.55	1.17	1.70
0.75	1.40	0.71	0.94	1.17	0.61	0.48	0.68
0.88	0.40	0.36	0.55	0.78	1.41	0.99	0.58
1.36	1.24	0.58	1.19	0.61	0.69	1.15	0.71
1.59	0.46	0.46	0.28	1.36	0.78	0.37	0.78
1.18	0.77	0.73	1.06	0.70	0.95	0.63	0.78
0.74	1.50	0.80	0.60	0.33	2.00	0.42	1.11
1.99	0.99	1.16	0.57	0.30	1.95	0.31	
0.75	0.58	0.73	0.71	1.48	1.70	0.29	

c. First Tube Insertion Time Groupings

Class Limits (Minutes)	Participants
0–0.06	42
0.07–0.12	48
0.13–0.18	22
0.19–0.24	13
0.25–0.30	10
0.31–0.36	9
0.37–0.42	4
0.43–0.48	0
0.49–0.54	3
0.55–0.60	1
0.61–0.66	0
0.67–0.72	0
0.73–0.78	2
0.79–0.84	2
0.85–0.90	1
0.91–0.96	1

d. Total Tube Insertion Time Groupings

Class Limits (Minutes)	Participants
0–0.20	0
0.21–0.40	15
0.41–0.60	33
0.61–0.80	34
0.81–1.00	21
1.01–1.20	19
1.21–1.40	9
1.41–1.60	9
1.61–1.80	6
1.81–2.00	4
2.01–2.20	2
2.21–2.40	3
2.41–2.60	1
2.61–2.80	1
2.81–3.00	1

Data Set 2

The inherent nature of development programs frequently requires estimates for various portions of the program, such as research, engineering, tooling, and so forth. The effort expended during the engineering portion of a development program is quite large. Research was conducted in such a program to estimate the engineering requirements more accurately. Historical data for eleven independent variables were developed from which three independent variables were finally selected as being of primary importance. Multiple regression was utilized in the analysis of the raw data. The data presented below have been coded to simplify calculations. The dependent variable is denoted as y, while x_1, x_2 and x_3 denote the independent variables.

y	x_1	x_2	x_3
7.32	6.35	6.54	77.5
10.62	12.78	9.61	418.8
17.93	13.84	3.77	143.1
16.12	15.10	5.41	418.8
13.34	18.42	6.82	454.3
16.84	31.83	5.66	574.7
14.66	35.07	8.80	356.7
20.63	45.56	6.43	521.8

Data Set 3

In the automatic welding of rare alloys, it may be necessary, because of the scarcity and expense of materials, to determine with very few samples the control variables which affect the mechanical properties of the welds. These data are but a part of a set of data from just such an experiment where seven independent control variables were monitored. Here x_1 and x_2 are operating voltage and electrode current, respectively, and their product x_1x_2 is power. The dependent variable y is the mechanical property of elongation in inches per inch.

y	x_1	x_2	x_1x_2
2.3	10.7	167	1,786.9
1.3	10.7	166	1,776.2
1.5	10.8	166	1,792.8
3.7	11.6	170	1,972.0
3.5	11.0	185	2,035.0
4.5	11.5	178	2,047.0
4.7	11.0	185	2,035.0
3.3	11.0	182	2,035.0
2.3	12.2	182	2,220.4
4.2	11.2	180	2,016.0

Data Set 4

Plastic foam is sometimes "grown" in blocks and used as insulation against shock. Therefore, it is desirable to know the uniformity of the foam. This uniformity can be tested by crushing samples of the foam taken from various positions in the block and measuring the compressive yield strength. A block was "grown" and sliced into nine layers. Each layer was then cut into four parts (upper-left corner, upper-right, etc.) and denoted as position *A*, *B*, *C* or *D*. The samples were then crushed and the data recorded. Layer 1 is expected to be the most dense since it was at the bottom of the block.

RL-2405 Plastic Foam

Compressive Yield (psi)

Layer No.	Position			
	A	*B*	*C*	*D*
1	142.9	140.1	141.3	142.2
2	139.1	138.3	141.6	143.2
3	138.6	137.7	140.8	145.5
4	136.4	137.1	139.2	143.2
5	138.2	140.2	141.9	144.5
6	139.2	140.3	141.8	144.6
7	134.9	135.0	136.6	138.6
8	132.8	132.4	133.7	135.5
9	125.0	125.0	126.5	127.5

Data Set 5

The uniformity of a process from application to application, as well as the ability to retain the original process conditions, can be quite critical in certain problems. The following set of data is taken from an environmental test of a particular adhesive. The ten sets of six specimens were stored for the various times under 20° F and 55 per cent relative humidity to see if there was, in fact, a degradation in the adhesive properties. The values represent yield strength of the specimens in psi.

Specimen No.	Days Stored at 20° F and 55% RH					
	0	1	2	3	4	5
1	3,560	3,180	3,470	3,520	3,720	3,310
2	3,630	3,080	3,620	3,960	4,120	3,140
3	3,800	3,400	3,466	4,040	4,040	3,660
4	3,880	3,820	3,460	3,600	4,200	3,400
5	3,840	3,480	3,760	3,899	3,400	3,760
6	3,600	2,980	3,050	3,880	3,800	3,320
7	4,020	3,380	3,480	4,000	3,920	4,140
8	4,020	3,400	3,100	3,880	3,960	3,240
9	4,240	2,820	2,984	3,720	3,840	3,240
10	3,660	3,600	2,950	3,760	3,800	3,520

Cumulative Probabilities of the Normal Probability Distributio
(Areas under the Normal Curve from $-\infty$ to z)

z	.00	.01	.02	.03	.04	.05	.06	.07	.08	.09
.0	.5000	.5040	.5080	.5120	.5160	.5199	.5239	.5279	.5319	.5359
.1	.5398	.5438	.5478	.5517	.5557	.5596	.5636	.5675	.5714	.5753
.2	.5793	.5832	.5871	.5910	.5948	.5987	.6026	.6064	.6103	.6141
.3	.6179	.6217	.6255	.6293	.6331	.6368	.6406	.6443	.6480	.6517
.4	.6554	.6591	.6628	.6664	.6700	.6736	.6772	.6808	.6844	.6879
.5	.6915	.6950	.6985	.7019	.7054	.7088	.7123	.7157	.7190	.7224
.6	.7257	.7291	.7324	.7357	.7389	.7422	.7454	.7486	.7517	.7549
.7	.7580	.7611	.7642	.7673	.7704	.7734	.7764	.7794	.7823	.7852
.8	.7881	.7910	.7939	.7967	.7995	.8023	.8051	.8078	.8106	.8133
.9	.8159	.8186	.8212	.8238	.8264	.8289	.8315	.8340	.8365	.8389
1.0	.8413	.8438	.8461	.8485	.8508	.8531	.8554	.8577	.8599	.8621
1.1	.8643	.8665	.8686	.8708	.8729	.8749	.8770	.8790	.8810	.8830
1.2	.8849	.8869	.8888	.8907	.8925	.8944	.8962	.8980	.8997	.9015
1.3	.9032	.9049	.9066	.9082	.9099	.9115	.9131	.9147	.9162	.9177
1.4	.9192	.9207	.9222	.9236	.9251	.9265	.9279	.9292	.9306	.9319
1.5	.9332	.9345	.9357	.9370	.9382	.9394	.9406	.9418	.9429	.9441
1.6	.9452	.9463	.9474	.9484	.9495	.9505	.9515	.9525	.9535	.9545
1.7	.9554	.9564	.9573	.9582	.9591	.9599	.9608	.9616	.9625	.9633
1.8	.9641	.9649	.9656	.9664	.9671	.9678	.9686	.9693	.9699	.9706
1.9	.9713	.9719	.9726	.9732	.9738	.9744	.9750	.9756	.9761	.9767
2.0	.9772	.9778	.9783	.9788	.9793	.9798	.9803	.9808	.9812	.9817
2.1	.9821	.9826	.9830	.9834	.9838	.9842	.9846	.9850	.9854	.9857
2.2	.9861	.9864	.9868	.9871	.9875	.9878	.9881	.9884	.9887	.9890
2.3	.9893	.9896	.9898	.9901	.9904	.9906	.9909	.9911	.9913	.9916
2.4	.9918	.9920	.9922	.9925	.9927	.9929	.9931	.9932	.9934	.9936
2.5	.9938	.9940	.9941	.9943	.9945	.9946	.9948	.9949	.9951	.9952
2.6	.9953	.9955	.9956	.3957	.9959	.9960	.9961	.9962	.9963	.9964
2.7	.9965	.9966	.9967	.9968	.9969	.9970	.9971	.9972	.9973	.9974
2.8	.9974	.9975	.9976	.9977	.9977	.9978	.9979	.9979	.9980	.9981
2.9	.9981	.9982	.9982	.9983	.9984	.9984	.9985	.9985	.9986	.9986
3.0	.9987	.9987	.9987	.9988	.9988	.9989	.9989	.9989	.9990	.9990
3.1	.9990	.9991	.9991	.9991	.9992	.9992	.9992	.9992	.9993	.9993
3.2	.9993	.9993	.9994	.9994	.9994	.9994	.9994	.9995	.9995	.9995
3.3	.9995	.9995	.9995	.9996	.9996	.9996	.9996	.9996	.9996	.9997
3.4	.9997	.9997	.9997	.9997	.9997	.9997	.9997	.9997	.9997	.9998

$\bar{z}$	1.282	1.645	1.960	2.326	2.576	3.090	3.291	3.891	4.417
$F(z)$	.90	.95	.975	.99	.995	.999	.9995	.99995	.999995
$2[1 - F(z)]$	.20	.10	.05	.02	.01	.002	.001	.0001	.00001

* Appendix E is reprinted with permission from A. M. Mood, *Introduction to the Theory of Statistics* (New York: McGraw-Hill Book Co., Inc., 1950), p. 423.

APPENDIX F
Percentage Points of the χ^2 Distribution*

ν\P	0.995	0.990	0.975	0.950	0.900	0.800	0.700	0.500	0.300	0.200	0.10	0.05	0.025	0.010	0.005	0.001
1	0.0^4393	0.0^3157	0.0^3982	0.00393	0.0158	0.0642	0.148	0.455	1.07	1.64	2.71	3.84	5.02	6.63	7.88	10.8
2	0.0100	0.0201	0.0506	0.103	0.211	0.446	0.713	1.39	2.41	3.22	4.61	5.99	7.38	9.21	10.6	13.8
3	0.0717	0.115	0.216	0.352	0.584	1.01	1.42	2.37	3.67	4.64	6.25	7.82	9.35	11.3	12.8	16.3
4	0.207	0.297	0.484	0.711	1.06	1.65	2.20	3.36	4.88	5.99	7.78	9.49	11.1	13.3	14.9	18.5
5	0.412	0.554	0.831	1.15	1.61	2.34	3.00	4.35	6.06	7.29	9.24	11.1	12.8	15.1	16.7	20.5
6	0.676	0.872	1.24	1.64	2.20	3.07	3.83	5.35	7.23	8.56	10.6	12.6	14.4	16.8	18.5	22.5
7	0.989	1.24	1.69	2.17	2.83	3.82	4.67	6.35	8.38	9.80	12.0	14.1	16.0	18.5	20.3	24.3
8	1.34	1.65	2.18	2.73	3.49	4.59	5.53	7.34	9.52	11.0	13.4	15.5	17.5	20.1	22.0	26.1
9	1.73	2.09	2.70	3.33	4.17	5.38	6.39	8.34	10.7	12.2	14.7	16.9	19.0	21.7	23.6	27.9
10	2.16	2.56	3.25	3.94	4.87	6.18	7.27	9.34	11.8	13.4	16.0	18.3	20.5	23.2	25.2	29.6
11	2.60	3.05	3.82	4.57	5.58	6.99	8.15	10.3	12.9	14.6	17.3	19.7	21.9	24.7	26.8	31.3
12	3.07	3.57	4.40	5.23	6.30	7.81	9.03	11.3	14.0	15.8	18.5	21.0	23.3	26.2	28.3	32.9
13	3.57	4.11	5.01	5.89	7.04	8.63	9.93	12.3	15.1	17.0	19.8	22.4	24.7	27.7	29.8	34.5
14	4.07	4.66	5.63	6.57	7.79	9.47	10.8	13.3	16.2	18.2	21.1	23.7	26.1	29.1	31.3	36.1
15	4.60	5.23	6.26	7.26	8.55	10.3	11.7	14.3	17.3	19.3	22.3	25.0	27.5	30.6	32.8	37.7
16	5.14	5.81	6.91	7.96	9.31	11.2	12.6	15.3	18.4	20.5	23.5	26.3	28.8	32.0	34.3	39.3
17	5.70	6.41	7.56	8.67	10.1	12.0	13.5	16.3	19.5	21.6	24.8	27.6	30.2	33.4	35.7	40.8
18	6.26	7.01	8.23	9.39	10.9	12.9	14.4	17.3	20.6	22.8	26.0	28.9	31.5	34.8	37.2	42.3
19	6.84	7.63	8.91	10.1	11.7	13.7	15.4	18.3	21.7	23.9	27.2	30.1	32.9	36.2	38.6	43.8
20	7.43	8.26	9.59	10.9	12.4	14.6	16.3	19.3	22.8	25.0	28.4	31.4	34.2	37.6	40.0	45.3
21	8.03	8.90	10.3	11.6	13.2	15.4	17.2	20.3	23.9	26.2	29.6	32.7	35.5	38.9	41.4	46.8
22	8.64	9.54	11.0	12.3	14.0	16.3	18.1	21.3	24.9	27.3	30.8	33.9	36.8	40.3	42.8	48.3
23	9.26	10.2	11.7	13.1	14.8	17.2	19.0	22.3	26.0	28.4	32.0	35.2	38.1	41.6	44.2	49.7
24	9.89	10.9	12.4	13.8	15.7	18.1	19.9	23.3	27.1	29.6	33.2	36.4	39.4	43.0	45.6	51.2
25	10.5	11.5	13.1	14.6	16.5	18.9	20.9	24.3	28.2	30.7	34.4	37.7	40.6	44.3	46.9	52.6
26	11.2	12.2	13.8	15.4	17.3	19.8	21.8	25.3	29.2	31.8	35.6	38.9	41.9	45.6	48.3	54.1
27	11.8	12.9	14.6	16.2	18.1	20.7	22.7	26.3	30.3	32.9	36.7	40.1	43.2	47.0	49.6	55.5
28	12.5	13.6	15.3	16.9	18.9	21.6	23.6	27.3	31.4	34.0	37.9	41.3	44.5	48.3	51.0	56.9
29	13.1	14.3	16.0	17.7	19.8	22.5	24.6	28.3	32.5	35.1	39.1	42.6	45.7	49.6	52.3	58.3
30	13.8	15.0	16.8	18.5	20.6	23.4	25.5	29.3	33.5	36.3	40.3	43.8	47.0	50.9	53.7	59.7

* Columns 0.995, 0.975, 0.025, and 0.005 are abridged with permission from Catherine M. Thompson, "Table of Percentage Points of the χ^2 Distribution," *Biometrika*, Vol. XXXII, Part II (1941), pp. 188–89. The remainder of the table is abridged with permission from Table IV of R. A. Fisher and F. Yates, *Statistical Tables for Biological, Agricultural and Medical Research* (Edinburgh: Oliver & Boyd, Ltd.).

177

APPENDIX G
Critical Values for the F Distribution*

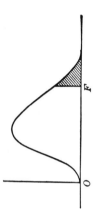

5% (Roman Type) and 1% (Bold-Face Type) Points for the Distribution of F

Degrees of freedom for lesser mean square (ν_2)	Degrees of freedom for greater mean square (ν_1)																							
	1	2	3	4	5	6	7	8	9	10	11	12	14	16	20	24	30	40	50	75	100	200	500	∞
1	161 **4052**	200 **4999**	216 **5403**	225 **5625**	230 **5764**	234 **5859**	237 **5928**	239 **5981**	241 **6022**	242 **6056**	243 **6082**	244 **6106**	245 **6142**	246 **6169**	248 **6208**	249 **6234**	250 **6258**	251 **6286**	252 **6302**	253 **6323**	253 **6334**	254 **6352**	254 **6361**	254 **6366**
2	18.51 **98.49**	19.00 **99.01**	19.16 **99.17**	19.25 **99.25**	19.30 **99.30**	19.33 **99.33**	19.36 **99.34**	19.37 **99.36**	19.38 **99.38**	19.39 **99.40**	19.40 **99.41**	19.41 **99.42**	19.42 **99.43**	19.43 **99.44**	19.44 **99.45**	19.45 **99.46**	19.46 **99.47**	19.47 **99.48**	19.47 **99.48**	19.48 **99.49**	19.49 **99.49**	19.49 **99.49**	19.50 **99.50**	19.50 **99.50**
3	10.13 **34.12**	9.55 **30.81**	9.28 **29.46**	9.12 **28.71**	9.01 **28.24**	8.94 **27.91**	8.88 **27.67**	8.84 **27.49**	8.81 **27.34**	8.78 **27.23**	8.76 **27.13**	8.74 **27.05**	8.71 **26.92**	8.69 **26.83**	8.66 **26.69**	8.64 **26.60**	8.62 **26.50**	8.60 **26.41**	8.58 **26.30**	8.57 **26.27**	8.56 **26.23**	8.54 **26.18**	8.54 **26.14**	8.53 **26.12**
4	7.71 **21.20**	6.94 **18.00**	6.59 **16.69**	6.39 **15.98**	6.26 **15.52**	6.16 **15.21**	6.09 **14.98**	6.04 **14.80**	6.00 **14.66**	5.96 **14.54**	5.93 **14.45**	5.91 **14.37**	5.87 **14.24**	5.84 **14.15**	5.80 **14.02**	5.77 **13.93**	5.74 **13.83**	5.71 **13.74**	5.70 **13.69**	5.68 **13.61**	5.66 **13.57**	5.65 **13.52**	5.64 **13.48**	5.63 **13.46**
5	6.61 **16.26**	5.79 **13.27**	5.41 **12.06**	5.19 **11.39**	5.05 **10.97**	4.95 **10.67**	4.88 **10.45**	4.82 **10.27**	4.78 **10.15**	4.74 **10.05**	4.70 **9.96**	4.68 **9.89**	4.64 **9.77**	4.60 **9.68**	4.56 **9.55**	4.53 **9.47**	4.50 **9.38**	4.46 **9.29**	4.44 **9.24**	4.42 **9.17**	4.40 **9.13**	4.38 **9.07**	4.37 **9.04**	4.36 **9.02**
6	5.99 **13.74**	5.14 **10.92**	4.76 **9.78**	4.53 **9.15**	4.39 **8.75**	4.28 **8.47**	4.21 **8.26**	4.15 **8.10**	4.10 **7.98**	4.06 **7.87**	4.03 **7.79**	4.00 **7.72**	3.96 **7.60**	3.92 **7.52**	3.87 **7.39**	3.84 **7.31**	3.81 **7.23**	3.77 **7.14**	3.75 **7.09**	3.72 **7.02**	3.71 **6.99**	3.69 **6.94**	3.68 **6.90**	3.67 **6.88**
7	5.59 **12.25**	4.74 **9.55**	4.35 **8.45**	4.12 **7.85**	3.97 **7.46**	3.87 **7.19**	3.79 **7.00**	3.73 **6.84**	3.68 **6.71**	3.63 **6.62**	3.60 **6.54**	3.57 **6.47**	3.52 **6.35**	3.49 **6.27**	3.44 **6.15**	3.41 **6.07**	3.38 **5.98**	3.34 **5.90**	3.32 **5.85**	3.29 **5.78**	3.28 **5.75**	3.25 **5.70**	3.24 **5.67**	3.23 **5.65**
8	5.32 **11.26**	4.46 **8.65**	4.07 **7.59**	3.84 **7.01**	3.69 **6.63**	3.58 **6.37**	3.50 **6.19**	3.44 **6.03**	3.39 **5.91**	3.34 **5.82**	3.31 **5.74**	3.28 **5.67**	3.23 **5.56**	3.20 **5.48**	3.15 **5.36**	3.12 **5.28**	3.08 **5.20**	3.05 **5.11**	3.03 **5.06**	3.00 **5.00**	2.98 **4.96**	2.96 **4.91**	2.94 **4.88**	2.93 **4.86**
9	5.12 **10.56**	4.26 **8.02**	3.86 **6.99**	3.63 **6.42**	3.48 **6.06**	3.37 **5.80**	3.29 **5.62**	3.23 **5.47**	3.18 **5.35**	3.13 **5.26**	3.10 **5.18**	3.07 **5.11**	3.02 **5.00**	2.98 **4.92**	2.93 **4.80**	2.90 **4.73**	2.86 **4.64**	2.82 **4.56**	2.80 **4.51**	2.77 **4.45**	2.76 **4.41**	2.73 **4.36**	2.72 **4.33**	2.71 **4.31**

10	2.54 / 3.91	2.55 / 3.93	2.56 / 3.96	2.59 / 4.01	2.61 / 4.05	2.64 / 4.12	2.67 / 4.17	2.70 / 4.25	2.74 / 4.33	2.77 / 4.41	2.82 / 4.52	2.86 / 4.60	2.91 / 4.71	2.94 / 4.78	2.97 / 4.85	3.02 / 4.95	3.07 / 5.06	3.14 / 5.21	3.22 / 5.39	3.33 / 5.64	3.48 / 5.99	3.71 / 6.55	4.10 / 7.56	4.96 / 10.04
11	2.40 / 3.60	2.41 / 3.70	2.42 / 3.66	2.45 / 3.74	2.47 / 3.74	2.50 / 3.80	2.53 / 3.86	2.57 / 3.94	2.61 / 4.02	2.65 / 4.10	2.70 / 4.19	2.74 / 4.29	2.79 / 4.40	2.82 / 4.46	2.86 / 4.54	2.90 / 4.63	2.95 / 4.74	3.01 / 4.88	3.09 / 5.03	3.20 / 5.32	3.36 / 5.67	3.59 / 6.22	3.98 / 7.20	4.84 / 9.65
12	2.30 / 3.36	2.31 / 3.38	2.32 / 3.41	2.35 / 3.46	2.36 / 3.49	2.40 / 3.56	2.42 / 3.61	2.46 / 3.70	2.50 / 3.78	2.54 / 3.86	2.60 / 3.98	2.64 / 4.05	2.69 / 4.16	2.72 / 4.22	2.76 / 4.30	2.80 / 4.39	2.85 / 4.50	2.92 / 4.65	3.00 / 4.82	3.11 / 5.06	3.26 / 5.41	3.49 / 5.95	3.88 / 6.93	4.75 / 9.33
13	2.21 / 3.16	2.22 / 3.18	2.24 / 3.21	2.26 / 3.27	2.28 / 3.30	2.32 / 3.37	2.34 / 3.42	2.38 / 3.51	2.42 / 3.59	2.46 / 3.67	2.51 / 3.78	2.55 / 3.85	2.60 / 3.96	2.63 / 4.02	2.67 / 4.10	2.72 / 4.19	2.77 / 4.30	2.84 / 4.44	2.92 / 4.62	3.02 / 4.86	3.18 / 5.20	3.41 / 5.74	3.80 / 6.70	4.67 / 9.07
14	2.13 / 3.00	2.14 / 3.02	2.16 / 3.06	2.19 / 3.11	2.21 / 3.14	2.24 / 3.21	2.27 / 3.26	2.31 / 3.34	2.35 / 3.43	2.39 / 3.51	2.44 / 3.62	2.48 / 3.70	2.53 / 3.80	2.56 / 3.86	2.60 / 3.94	2.65 / 4.03	2.70 / 4.14	2.77 / 4.28	2.85 / 4.46	2.96 / 4.69	3.11 / 5.03	3.34 / 5.56	3.74 / 6.51	4.60 / 8.86
15	2.07 / 2.87	2.08 / 2.89	2.10 / 2.92	2.12 / 2.97	2.15 / 3.00	2.18 / 3.07	2.21 / 3.12	2.25 / 3.20	2.29 / 3.29	2.33 / 3.36	2.39 / 3.48	2.43 / 3.56	2.48 / 3.67	2.51 / 3.73	2.55 / 3.80	2.59 / 3.89	2.64 / 4.00	2.70 / 4.14	2.79 / 4.32	2.90 / 4.56	3.06 / 4.89	3.29 / 5.42	3.68 / 6.36	4.54 / 8.68
16	2.01 / 2.75	2.02 / 2.77	2.04 / 2.80	2.07 / 2.86	2.09 / 2.89	2.13 / 2.96	2.16 / 3.01	2.20 / 3.10	2.24 / 3.18	2.28 / 3.25	2.33 / 3.37	2.37 / 3.45	2.42 / 3.55	2.45 / 3.61	2.49 / 3.69	2.54 / 3.78	2.59 / 3.89	2.66 / 4.03	2.74 / 4.20	2.85 / 4.44	3.01 / 4.77	3.24 / 5.29	3.63 / 6.23	4.49 / 8.53
17	1.96 / 2.65	1.97 / 2.67	1.99 / 2.70	2.02 / 2.76	2.04 / 2.79	2.08 / 2.86	2.11 / 2.92	2.15 / 3.00	2.19 / 3.08	2.23 / 3.16	2.29 / 3.27	2.33 / 3.35	2.38 / 3.45	2.41 / 3.52	2.45 / 3.59	2.50 / 3.68	2.55 / 3.79	2.62 / 3.93	2.70 / 4.10	2.81 / 4.34	2.96 / 4.67	3.20 / 5.18	3.59 / 6.11	4.45 / 8.40
18	1.92 / 2.57	1.93 / 2.59	1.95 / 2.62	1.98 / 2.68	2.00 / 2.71	2.04 / 2.78	2.07 / 2.83	2.11 / 2.91	2.15 / 3.00	2.19 / 3.07	2.25 / 3.19	2.29 / 3.27	2.34 / 3.37	2.37 / 3.44	2.41 / 3.51	2.46 / 3.60	2.51 / 3.71	2.58 / 3.85	2.66 / 4.01	2.77 / 4.25	2.93 / 4.58	3.16 / 5.09	3.55 / 6.01	4.41 / 8.28
19	1.88 / 2.49	1.90 / 2.51	1.91 / 2.54	1.94 / 2.60	1.96 / 2.63	2.00 / 2.70	2.02 / 2.76	2.07 / 2.84	2.11 / 2.92	2.15 / 3.00	2.21 / 3.12	2.26 / 3.19	2.31 / 3.30	2.34 / 3.36	2.38 / 3.43	2.43 / 3.52	2.48 / 3.63	2.55 / 3.77	2.63 / 3.94	2.74 / 4.17	2.90 / 4.50	3.13 / 5.01	3.52 / 5.93	4.38 / 8.18
20	1.84 / 2.42	1.85 / 2.44	1.87 / 2.47	1.90 / 2.53	1.92 / 2.56	1.96 / 2.63	1.99 / 2.69	2.04 / 2.77	2.08 / 2.86	2.12 / 2.94	2.18 / 3.05	2.23 / 3.13	2.28 / 3.23	2.31 / 3.30	2.35 / 3.37	2.40 / 3.45	2.45 / 3.56	2.52 / 3.71	2.60 / 3.87	2.71 / 4.10	2.87 / 4.43	3.10 / 4.94	3.49 / 5.85	4.35 / 8.10
21	1.81 / 2.36	1.82 / 2.38	1.84 / 2.42	1.87 / 2.47	1.89 / 2.51	1.93 / 2.58	1.96 / 2.63	2.00 / 2.72	2.05 / 2.80	2.09 / 2.88	2.15 / 2.99	2.20 / 3.07	2.25 / 3.17	2.28 / 3.24	2.32 / 3.31	2.37 / 3.40	2.42 / 3.51	2.49 / 3.65	2.57 / 3.81	2.68 / 4.04	2.84 / 4.37	3.07 / 4.87	3.47 / 5.78	4.32 / 8.02
22	1.78 / 2.31	1.80 / 2.33	1.81 / 2.37	1.84 / 2.42	1.87 / 2.46	1.91 / 2.53	1.93 / 2.58	1.98 / 2.67	2.03 / 2.75	2.07 / 2.83	2.13 / 2.94	2.18 / 3.02	2.23 / 3.12	2.26 / 3.18	2.30 / 3.26	2.35 / 3.35	2.40 / 3.45	2.47 / 3.59	2.55 / 3.76	2.66 / 3.99	2.82 / 4.31	3.05 / 4.82	3.44 / 5.72	4.30 / 7.94
23	1.76 / 2.26	1.77 / 2.28	1.79 / 2.32	1.82 / 2.37	1.84 / 2.41	1.88 / 2.48	1.91 / 2.53	1.96 / 2.62	2.00 / 2.70	2.04 / 2.78	2.10 / 2.89	2.14 / 2.97	2.20 / 3.07	2.24 / 3.14	2.28 / 3.21	2.32 / 3.30	2.38 / 3.41	2.45 / 3.54	2.53 / 3.71	2.64 / 3.94	2.80 / 4.26	3.03 / 4.76	3.42 / 5.66	4.28 / 7.88
24	1.73 / 2.21	1.74 / 2.23	1.76 / 2.27	1.80 / 2.33	1.82 / 2.36	1.86 / 2.44	1.89 / 2.49	1.94 / 2.58	1.98 / 2.66	2.02 / 2.74	2.09 / 2.85	2.13 / 2.93	2.18 / 3.03	2.22 / 3.09	2.26 / 3.17	2.30 / 3.25	2.36 / 3.36	2.43 / 3.50	2.51 / 3.67	2.62 / 3.90	2.78 / 4.22	3.01 / 4.72	3.40 / 5.61	4.26 / 7.82
25	1.71 / 2.17	1.72 / 2.19	1.74 / 2.23	1.77 / 2.29	1.80 / 2.32	1.84 / 2.40	1.87 / 2.45	1.92 / 2.54	1.96 / 2.62	2.00 / 2.70	2.06 / 2.81	2.11 / 2.89	2.16 / 2.99	2.20 / 3.05	2.24 / 3.13	2.28 / 3.21	2.34 / 3.32	2.41 / 3.46	2.49 / 3.63	2.60 / 3.86	2.76 / 4.18	2.99 / 4.68	3.38 / 5.57	4.24 / 7.77
26	1.69 / 2.13	1.70 / 2.15	1.72 / 2.19	1.76 / 2.25	1.78 / 2.28	1.82 / 2.36	1.85 / 2.41	1.90 / 2.50	1.95 / 2.58	1.99 / 2.66	2.05 / 2.77	2.10 / 2.86	2.15 / 2.96	2.18 / 3.02	2.22 / 3.09	2.27 / 3.17	2.32 / 3.29	2.39 / 3.42	2.47 / 3.59	2.59 / 3.82	2.74 / 4.14	2.89 / 4.64	3.37 / 5.53	4.22 / 7.72

APPENDIX G (continued)

5% (Roman Type) and 1% (Bold-Face Type) Points for the Distribution of F

Degrees of freedom for greater mean square

Degrees of freedom for lesser mean square	1	2	3	4	5	6	7	8	9	10	11	12	14	16	20	24	30	40	50	75	100	200	500	∞
27	4.21 / **7.68**	3.35 / **5.49**	2.96 / **4.60**	2.73 / **4.11**	2.57 / **3.79**	2.46 / **3.56**	2.37 / **3.39**	2.30 / **3.26**	2.25 / **3.14**	2.20 / **3.06**	2.16 / **2.98**	2.13 / **2.93**	2.08 / **2.83**	2.03 / **2.74**	1.97 / **2.63**	1.93 / **2.55**	1.88 / **2.47**	1.84 / **2.38**	1.80 / **2.33**	1.76 / **2.25**	1.74 / **2.21**	1.71 / **2.16**	1.68 / **2.12**	1.67 / **2.10**
28	4.20 / **7.64**	3.34 / **5.45**	2.95 / **4.57**	2.71 / **4.07**	2.56 / **3.76**	2.44 / **3.53**	2.36 / **3.36**	2.29 / **3.23**	2.24 / **3.11**	2.19 / **3.03**	2.15 / **2.95**	2.12 / **2.90**	2.06 / **2.80**	2.02 / **2.71**	1.96 / **2.60**	1.91 / **2.52**	1.87 / **2.44**	1.81 / **2.35**	1.78 / **2.30**	1.75 / **2.22**	1.72 / **2.18**	1.69 / **2.13**	1.67 / **2.09**	1.65 / **2.06**
29	4.18 / **7.60**	3.33 / **5.52**	2.93 / **4.54**	2.70 / **4.04**	2.54 / **3.73**	2.43 / **3.50**	2.35 / **3.33**	2.28 / **3.20**	2.22 / **3.08**	2.18 / **3.00**	2.14 / **2.92**	2.10 / **2.87**	2.05 / **2.77**	2.00 / **2.68**	1.94 / **2.57**	1.90 / **2.49**	1.85 / **2.41**	1.80 / **2.32**	1.77 / **2.27**	1.73 / **2.19**	1.71 / **2.15**	1.68 / **2.10**	1.65 / **2.06**	1.64 / **2.03**
30	4.17 / **7.56**	3.32 / **5.39**	2.92 / **4.51**	2.69 / **4.02**	2.53 / **3.70**	2.42 / **3.47**	2.34 / **3.30**	2.27 / **3.17**	2.21 / **3.06**	2.16 / **2.98**	2.12 / **2.90**	2.09 / **2.84**	2.04 / **2.74**	1.99 / **2.66**	1.93 / **2.55**	1.89 / **2.47**	1.84 / **2.38**	1.79 / **2.29**	1.76 / **2.24**	1.72 / **2.16**	1.69 / **2.13**	1.66 / **2.07**	1.64 / **2.03**	1.62 / **2.01**
32	4.15 / **7.50**	3.30 / **5.34**	2.90 / **4.46**	2.67 / **3.97**	2.51 / **3.66**	2.40 / **3.42**	2.32 / **3.25**	2.25 / **3.12**	2.19 / **3.01**	2.14 / **2.94**	2.10 / **2.86**	2.07 / **2.80**	2.02 / **2.70**	1.97 / **2.62**	1.91 / **2.51**	1.86 / **2.42**	1.82 / **2.34**	1.76 / **2.25**	1.74 / **2.20**	1.69 / **2.12**	1.67 / **2.08**	1.64 / **2.02**	1.61 / **1.98**	1.59 / **1.96**
34	4.13 / **7.44**	3.28 / **5.29**	2.88 / **4.42**	2.65 / **3.93**	2.49 / **3.61**	2.38 / **3.38**	2.30 / **3.21**	2.23 / **3.08**	2.17 / **2.97**	2.12 / **2.89**	2.08 / **2.82**	2.05 / **2.76**	2.00 / **2.66**	1.95 / **2.58**	1.89 / **2.47**	1.84 / **2.38**	1.80 / **2.30**	1.74 / **2.21**	1.71 / **2.15**	1.67 / **2.08**	1.64 / **2.04**	1.61 / **1.98**	1.59 / **1.94**	1.57 / **1.91**
36	4.11 / **7.39**	3.26 / **5.25**	2.86 / **4.38**	2.63 / **3.89**	2.48 / **3.58**	2.36 / **3.35**	2.28 / **3.18**	2.21 / **3.04**	2.15 / **2.94**	2.10 / **2.86**	2.06 / **2.78**	2.03 / **2.72**	1.98 / **2.62**	1.93 / **2.54**	1.87 / **2.43**	1.82 / **2.35**	1.78 / **2.26**	1.72 / **2.17**	1.69 / **2.12**	1.65 / **2.04**	1.62 / **2.00**	1.59 / **1.94**	1.56 / **1.90**	1.55 / **1.87**
38	4.10 / **7.35**	3.25 / **5.21**	2.85 / **4.34**	2.62 / **3.86**	2.46 / **3.54**	2.35 / **3.32**	2.26 / **3.15**	2.19 / **3.02**	2.14 / **2.91**	2.09 / **2.82**	2.05 / **2.75**	2.02 / **2.69**	1.96 / **2.59**	1.92 / **2.51**	1.85 / **2.40**	1.80 / **2.32**	1.76 / **2.22**	1.71 / **2.14**	1.67 / **2.08**	1.63 / **2.00**	1.60 / **1.97**	1.57 / **1.90**	1.54 / **1.86**	1.53 / **1.84**
40	4.08 / **7.31**	3.23 / **5.18**	2.84 / **4.31**	2.61 / **3.83**	2.45 / **3.51**	2.34 / **3.29**	2.25 / **3.12**	2.18 / **2.99**	2.12 / **2.88**	2.07 / **2.80**	2.04 / **2.73**	2.00 / **2.66**	1.95 / **2.56**	1.90 / **2.49**	1.84 / **2.37**	1.79 / **2.29**	1.74 / **2.20**	1.69 / **2.11**	1.66 / **2.05**	1.61 / **1.97**	1.59 / **1.94**	1.55 / **1.88**	1.53 / **1.84**	1.51 / **1.81**
42	4.07 / **7.27**	3.22 / **5.15**	2.83 / **4.29**	2.59 / **3.80**	2.44 / **3.49**	2.32 / **3.26**	2.24 / **3.10**	2.17 / **2.96**	2.11 / **2.86**	2.06 / **2.77**	2.02 / **2.70**	1.99 / **2.64**	1.94 / **2.54**	1.89 / **2.46**	1.82 / **2.35**	1.78 / **2.26**	1.73 / **2.17**	1.68 / **2.08**	1.64 / **2.02**	1.60 / **1.94**	1.57 / **1.91**	1.54 / **1.85**	1.51 / **1.80**	1.49 / **1.78**
44	4.06 / **7.24**	3.21 / **5.12**	2.82 / **4.26**	2.58 / **3.78**	2.43 / **3.46**	2.31 / **3.24**	2.23 / **3.07**	2.16 / **2.94**	2.10 / **2.84**	2.05 / **2.75**	2.01 / **2.68**	1.98 / **2.62**	1.92 / **2.52**	1.88 / **2.44**	1.81 / **2.32**	1.76 / **2.24**	1.72 / **2.15**	1.66 / **2.06**	1.63 / **2.00**	1.58 / **1.92**	1.56 / **1.88**	1.52 / **1.82**	1.50 / **1.78**	1.48 / **1.75**
46	4.05 / **7.21**	3.20 / **5.10**	2.81 / **4.24**	2.57 / **3.76**	2.42 / **3.44**	2.30 / **3.22**	2.22 / **3.05**	2.14 / **2.92**	2.09 / **2.82**	2.04 / **2.73**	2.00 / **2.66**	1.97 / **2.60**	1.91 / **2.50**	1.87 / **2.42**	1.80 / **2.30**	1.75 / **2.22**	1.71 / **2.13**	1.65 / **2.04**	1.62 / **1.98**	1.57 / **1.90**	1.54 / **1.86**	1.51 / **1.80**	1.48 / **1.76**	1.46 / **1.72**
48	4.04 / **7.19**	3.19 / **5.08**	2.80 / **4.22**	2.56 / **3.74**	2.41 / **3.42**	2.30 / **3.20**	2.21 / **3.04**	2.14 / **2.90**	2.08 / **2.80**	2.03 / **2.71**	1.99 / **2.64**	1.96 / **2.58**	1.90 / **2.48**	1.86 / **2.40**	1.79 / **2.28**	1.74 / **2.20**	1.70 / **2.11**	1.64 / **2.02**	1.61 / **1.96**	1.56 / **1.88**	1.53 / **1.84**	1.50 / **1.78**	1.47 / **1.73**	1.45 / **1.70**

n_2	1	2	3	4	5	6	7	8	9	10	11	12	14	16	20	24	30	40	50	75	100	200	500	∞
50	4.03 **7.17**	3.18 **5.06**	2.79 **4.20**	2.56 **3.72**	2.40 **3.41**	2.29 **3.18**	2.20 **3.02**	2.13 **2.88**	2.07 **2.78**	2.02 **2.70**	1.98 **2.62**	1.95 **2.56**	1.90 **2.46**	1.85 **2.39**	1.78 **2.26**	1.74 **2.18**	1.69 **2.10**	1.63 **2.00**	1.60 **1.94**	1.55 **1.86**	1.52 **1.82**	1.48 **1.76**	1.46 **1.71**	1.44 **1.68**
55	4.02 **7.12**	3.17 **5.01**	2.78 **4.16**	2.54 **3.68**	2.38 **3.37**	2.27 **3.15**	2.18 **2.98**	2.11 **2.85**	2.05 **2.75**	2.00 **2.66**	1.97 **2.59**	1.93 **2.53**	1.88 **2.43**	1.83 **2.35**	1.76 **2.23**	1.72 **2.15**	1.67 **2.06**	1.61 **1.96**	1.58 **1.90**	1.52 **1.82**	1.50 **1.78**	1.46 **1.71**	1.43 **1.66**	1.41 **1.64**
60	4.00 **7.08**	3.15 **4.98**	2.76 **4.13**	2.52 **3.65**	2.37 **3.34**	2.25 **3.12**	2.17 **2.95**	2.10 **2.82**	2.04 **2.72**	1.99 **2.63**	1.95 **2.56**	1.92 **2.50**	1.86 **2.40**	1.81 **2.32**	1.75 **2.20**	1.70 **2.12**	1.65 **2.03**	1.59 **1.93**	1.56 **1.87**	1.50 **1.79**	1.48 **1.74**	1.44 **1.68**	1.41 **1.63**	1.39 **1.60**
65	3.99 **7.04**	3.14 **4.95**	2.75 **4.10**	2.51 **3.62**	2.36 **3.31**	2.24 **3.09**	2.15 **2.93**	2.08 **2.79**	2.02 **2.70**	1.98 **2.61**	1.94 **2.54**	1.90 **2.47**	1.85 **2.37**	1.80 **2.30**	1.73 **2.18**	1.68 **2.09**	1.63 **2.00**	1.57 **1.90**	1.54 **1.84**	1.49 **1.76**	1.46 **1.71**	1.42 **1.64**	1.39 **1.60**	1.37 **1.56**
70	3.98 **7.01**	3.13 **4.92**	2.74 **4.08**	2.50 **3.60**	2.35 **3.29**	2.23 **3.07**	2.14 **2.91**	2.07 **2.77**	2.01 **2.67**	1.97 **2.59**	1.93 **2.51**	1.89 **2.45**	1.84 **2.35**	1.79 **2.28**	1.72 **2.15**	1.67 **2.07**	1.62 **1.98**	1.56 **1.88**	1.53 **1.82**	1.47 **1.74**	1.45 **1.69**	1.40 **1.62**	1.37 **1.56**	1.35 **1.53**
80	3.96 **6.96**	3.11 **4.88**	2.72 **4.04**	2.48 **3.56**	2.33 **3.25**	2.21 **3.04**	2.12 **2.87**	2.05 **2.74**	1.99 **2.64**	1.95 **2.55**	1.91 **2.48**	1.88 **2.41**	1.82 **2.32**	1.77 **2.24**	1.70 **2.11**	1.65 **2.03**	1.60 **1.94**	1.54 **1.84**	1.51 **1.78**	1.45 **1.70**	1.42 **1.65**	1.38 **1.57**	1.35 **1.52**	1.32 **1.49**
100	3.94 **6.90**	3.09 **4.82**	2.70 **3.98**	2.46 **3.51**	2.30 **3.20**	2.19 **2.99**	2.10 **2.82**	2.03 **2.69**	1.97 **2.59**	1.92 **2.51**	1.88 **2.43**	1.85 **2.36**	1.79 **2.26**	1.75 **2.19**	1.68 **2.06**	1.63 **1.98**	1.57 **1.89**	1.51 **1.79**	1.48 **1.73**	1.42 **1.64**	1.39 **1.59**	1.34 **1.51**	1.30 **1.46**	1.28 **1.43**
125	3.92 **6.84**	3.07 **4.78**	2.68 **3.94**	2.44 **3.47**	2.29 **3.17**	2.17 **2.95**	2.08 **2.79**	2.01 **2.65**	1.95 **2.56**	1.90 **2.47**	1.86 **2.40**	1.83 **2.33**	1.77 **2.23**	1.72 **2.15**	1.65 **2.03**	1.60 **1.94**	1.55 **1.85**	1.49 **1.75**	1.45 **1.68**	1.39 **1.59**	1.36 **1.54**	1.31 **1.46**	1.27 **1.40**	1.25 **1.37**
150	3.91 **6.81**	3.06 **4.75**	2.67 **3.91**	2.43 **3.44**	2.27 **3.13**	2.16 **2.92**	2.07 **2.76**	2.00 **2.62**	1.94 **2.53**	1.89 **2.44**	1.85 **2.37**	1.82 **2.30**	1.76 **2.20**	1.71 **2.12**	1.64 **2.00**	1.59 **1.91**	1.54 **1.83**	1.47 **1.72**	1.44 **1.66**	1.37 **1.56**	1.34 **1.51**	1.29 **1.43**	1.25 **1.37**	1.22 **1.33**
200	3.89 **6.76**	3.04 **4.71**	2.65 **3.88**	2.41 **3.41**	2.26 **3.11**	2.14 **2.90**	2.05 **2.73**	1.98 **2.60**	1.92 **2.50**	1.87 **2.41**	1.83 **2.34**	1.80 **2.28**	1.74 **2.17**	1.69 **2.09**	1.62 **1.97**	1.57 **1.88**	1.52 **1.79**	1.45 **1.69**	1.42 **1.62**	1.35 **1.53**	1.32 **1.48**	1.26 **1.39**	1.22 **1.33**	1.19 **1.28**
400	3.86 **6.70**	3.02 **4.66**	2.62 **3.83**	2.39 **3.36**	2.23 **3.06**	2.12 **2.85**	2.03 **2.69**	1.96 **2.55**	1.90 **2.46**	1.85 **2.37**	1.81 **2.29**	1.78 **2.23**	1.72 **2.12**	1.67 **2.04**	1.60 **1.92**	1.54 **1.84**	1.49 **1.74**	1.42 **1.64**	1.38 **1.57**	1.32 **1.47**	1.28 **1.42**	1.22 **1.32**	1.16 **1.24**	1.13 **1.19**
1000	3.85 **6.66**	3.00 **4.62**	2.61 **3.80**	2.38 **3.34**	2.22 **3.04**	2.10 **2.82**	2.02 **2.66**	1.95 **2.53**	1.89 **2.43**	1.84 **2.34**	1.80 **2.26**	1.76 **2.20**	1.70 **2.09**	1.65 **2.01**	1.58 **1.89**	1.53 **1.81**	1.47 **1.71**	1.41 **1.61**	1.36 **1.54**	1.30 **1.44**	1.26 **1.38**	1.19 **1.28**	1.13 **1.19**	1.08 **1.11**
∞	3.84 **6.64**	2.99 **4.60**	2.60 **3.78**	2.37 **3.32**	2.21 **3.02**	2.09 **2.80**	2.01 **2.64**	1.94 **2.51**	1.88 **2.41**	1.83 **2.32**	1.79 **2.24**	1.75 **2.18**	1.69 **2.07**	1.64 **1.99**	1.57 **1.87**	1.52 **1.79**	1.46 **1.69**	1.40 **1.59**	1.35 **1.52**	1.28 **1.41**	1.24 **1.36**	1.17 **1.25**	1.11 **1.15**	1.00 **1.00**

* Reprinted, by permission, from Snedecor, *Statistical Methods*, Collegiate Press, Iowa State College, Ames.

APPENDIX H

Percentage Points of the t Distribution*

(Probabilities refer to the sum of the two-tail areas. For a single tail, divide the probability by 2)

ν	Probability (P).												
	·9	·8	·7	·6	·5	·4	·3	·2	·1	·05	·02	·01	·001
1	·158	·325	·510	·727	1·000	1·376	1·963	3·078	6·314	12·706	31·821	63·657	636·619
2	·142	·289	·445	·617	·816	1·061	1·386	1·886	2·920	4·303	6·965	9·925	31·598
3	·137	·277	·424	·584	·765	·978	1·250	1·638	2·353	3·182	4·541	5·841	12·941
4	·134	·271	·414	·569	·741	·941	1·190	1·533	2·132	2·776	3·747	4·604	8·610
5	·132	·267	·408	·559	·727	·920	1·156	1·476	2·015	2·571	3·365	4·032	6·859
6	·131	·265	·404	·553	·718	·906	1·134	1·440	1·943	2·447	3·143	3·707	5·959
7	·130	·263	·402	·549	·711	·896	1·119	1·415	1·895	2·365	2·998	3·499	5·405
8	·130	·262	·399	·546	·706	·889	1·108	1·397	1·860	2·306	2·896	3·355	5·041
9	·129	·261	·398	·543	·703	·883	1·100	1·383	1·833	2·262	2·821	3·250	4·781
10	·129	·260	·397	·542	·700	·879	1·093	1·372	1·812	2·228	2·764	3·169	4·587
11	·129	·260	·396	·540	·697	·876	1·088	1·363	1·796	2·201	2·718	3·106	4·437
12	·128	·259	·395	·539	·695	·873	1·083	1·356	1·782	2·179	2·681	3·055	4·318
13	·128	·259	·394	·538	·694	·870	1·079	1·350	1·771	2·160	2·650	3·012	4·221
14	·128	·258	·393	·537	·692	·868	1·076	1·345	1·761	2·145	2·624	2·977	4·140
15	·128	·258	·393	·536	·691	·866	1·074	1·341	1·753	2·131	2·602	2·947	4·073
16	·128	·258	·392	·535	·690	·865	1·071	1·337	1·746	2·120	2·583	2·921	4·015
17	·128	·257	·392	·534	·689	·863	1·069	1·333	1·740	2·110	2·567	2·898	3·965
18	·127	·257	·392	·534	·688	·862	1·067	1·330	1·734	2·101	2·552	2·878	3·922
19	·127	·257	·391	·533	·688	·861	1·066	1·328	1·729	2·093	2·539	2·861	3·883
20	·127	·257	·391	·533	·687	·860	1·064	1·325	1·725	2·086	2·528	2·845	3·850
21	·127	·257	·391	·532	·686	·859	1·063	1·323	1·721	2·080	2·518	2·831	3·819
22	·127	·256	·390	·532	·686	·858	1·061	1·321	1·717	2·074	2·508	2·819	3·792
23	·127	·256	·390	·532	·685	·858	1·060	1·319	1·714	2·069	2·500	2·807	3·767
24	·127	·256	·390	·531	·685	·857	1·059	1·318	1·711	2·064	2·492	2·797	3·745
25	·127	·256	·390	·531	·684	·856	1·058	1·316	1·708	2·060	2·485	2·787	3·725
26	·127	·256	·390	·531	·684	·856	1·058	1·315	1·706	2·056	2·479	2·779	3·707
27	·127	·256	·389	·531	·684	·855	1·057	1·314	1·703	2·052	2·473	2·771	3·690
28	·127	·256	·389	·530	·683	·855	1·056	1·313	1·701	2·048	2·467	2·763	3·674
29	·127	·256	·389	·530	·683	·854	1·055	1·311	1·699	2·045	2·462	2·756	3·659
30	·127	·256	·389	·530	·683	·854	1·055	1·310	1·697	2·042	2·457	2·750	3·646
40	·126	·255	·388	·529	·681	·851	1·050	1·303	1·684	2·021	2·423	2·704	3·551
60	·126	·254	·387	·527	·679	·848	1·046	1·296	1·671	2·000	2·390	2·660	3·460
120	·126	·254	·386	·526	·677	·845	1·041	1·289	1·658	1·980	2·358	2·617	3·373
∞	·126	·253	·385	·524	·674	·842	1·036	1·282	1·645	1·960	2·326	2·576	3·291

* Appendix H is reprinted with permission from Table III of R. A. Fisher and F. Yates, *Statistical Tables for Biological, Agricultural and Medical Research* (Edinburgh: Oliver & Boyd, Ltd.).

APPENDIX I Table of Random Numbers*

```
22 17 68 65 84   68 95 23 92 35   87 02 22 57 51   61 09 43 95 06   58 24 82 03 47
19 36 27 59 46   13 79 93 37 55   39 77 32 77 09   85 52 05 30 62   47 83 51 62 74
16 77 23 02 77   09 61 87 25 21   28 06 24 25 93   16 71 13 59 78   23 05 47 47 25
78 43 76 71 61   20 44 90 32 64   97 67 63 99 61   46 38 03 93 22   69 81 21 99 21
03 28 28 26 08   73 37 32 04 05   69 30 16 09 05   88 69 58 28 99   35 07 44 75 47

93 22 53 64 39   07 10 63 76 35   87 03 04 79 88   08 13 13 85 51   55 34 57 72 69
78 76 58 54 74   92 38 70 96 92   52 06 79 79 45   82 63 18 27 44   69 66 92 19 09
23 68 35 26 00   99 53 93 61 28   52 70 05 48 34   56 65 05 61 86   90 92 10 70 80
15 39 25 70 99   93 86 52 77 65   15 33 59 05 28   22 87 26 07 47   86 96 98 29 06
58 71 96 30 24   18 46 23 34 27   85 13 99 24 44   49 18 09 79 49   74 16 32 23 02

57 35 27 33 72   24 53 63 94 09   41 10 76 47 91   44 04 95 49 66   39 60 04 59 81
48 50 86 54 48   22 06 34 72 52   82 21 15 65 20   33 29 94 71 11   15 91 29 12 03
61 96 48 95 03   07 16 39 33 66   98 56 10 56 79   77 21 30 27 12   90 49 22 23 62
36 93 89 41 26   29 70 83 63 51   99 74 20 52 36   87 09 41 15 09   98 60 16 03 03
18 87 00 42 31   57 90 12 02 07   23 47 37 17 31   54 08 01 88 63   39 41 88 92 10

88 56 53 27 59   33 35 72 67 47   77 34 55 45 70   08 18 27 38 90   16 95 86 70 75
09 72 95 84 29   49 41 31 06 70   42 38 06 45 18   64 84 73 31 65   52 53 37 97 15
12 96 88 17 31   65 19 69 02 83   60 75 86 90 68   24 64 19 35 51   56 61 87 39 12
85 94 57 24 16   92 09 84 38 76   22 00 27 69 85   29 81 94 78 70   21 94 47 90 12
38 64 43 59 98   98 77 87 68 07   91 51 67 62 44   40 98 05 93 78   23 32 65 41 18

53 44 09 42 72   00 41 86 79 79   68 47 22 00 20   35 55 31 51 51   00 83 63 22 55
40 76 66 26 84   57 99 99 90 37   36 63 32 08 58   37 40 13 68 97   87 64 81 07 83
02 17 79 18 05   12 59 52 57 02   22 07 90 47 03   28 14 11 30 79   20 69 22 40 98
95 17 82 06 53   31 51 10 96 46   92 06 88 07 77   56 11 50 81 69   40 23 72 51 39
35 76 22 42 92   96 11 83 44 80   34 68 35 48 77   33 42 40 90 60   73 96 53 97 86

26 29 13 56 41   85 47 04 66 08   34 72 57 59 13   82 43 80 46 15   38 26 61 70 04
77 80 20 75 82   72 82 32 99 90   63 95 73 76 63   89 73 44 99 05   48 67 26 43 18
46 40 66 44 52   91 36 74 43 53   30 82 13 54 00   78 45 63 98 35   55 03 36 67 68
37 56 08 18 09   77 53 84 46 47   31 91 18 95 58   24 16 74 11 53   44 10 13 85 57
61 65 61 68 66   37 27 47 39 19   84 83 70 07 48   53 21 40 06 71   95 06 79 88 54

93 43 69 64 07   34 18 04 52 35   56 27 09 24 86   61 85 53 83 45   19 90 70 99 00
21 96 60 12 99   11 20 99 45 18   48 13 93 55 34   18 37 79 49 90   65 97 38 20 46
95 20 47 97 97   27 37 83 28 71   00 06 41 41 74   45 89 09 39 84   51 67 11 52 49
97 86 21 78 73   10 65 81 92 59   58 76 17 14 97   04 76 62 16 17   17 95 70 45 80
69 92 06 34 13   59 71 74 17 32   27 55 10 24 19   23 71 82 13 74   63 52 52 01 41

04 31 17 21 56   33 73 99 19 87   26 72 39 27 67   53 77 57 68 93   60 61 97 22 61
61 06 98 03 91   87 14 77 43 96   43 00 65 98 50   45 60 33 01 07   98 99 46 50 47
85 93 85 86 88   72 87 08 62 40   16 06 10 89 20   23 21 34 74 97   76 38 03 29 63
21 74 32 47 45   73 96 07 94 52   09 65 90 77 47   25 76 16 19 33   53 05 70 53 30
15 69 53 82 80   79 96 23 53 10   65 39 07 16 29   45 33 02 43 70   02 87 40 41 45

02 89 08 04 49   20 21 14 68 86   87 63 93 95 17   11 29 01 95 80   35 14 97 35 33
87 18 15 89 79   85 43 01 72 73   08 61 74 51 69   89 74 39 82 15   94 51 33 41 67
98 83 71 94 22   59 97 50 99 52   08 52 85 08 40   87 80 61 65 31   91 51 80 32 44
10 08 58 21 66   72 68 49 29 31   89 85 84 46 06   59 73 19 85 23   65 09 29 75 63
47 90 56 10 08   88 02 84 27 83   42 29 72 23 19   66 56 45 65 79   20 71 53 20 25

22 85 61 68 90   49 64 92 85 44   16 40 12 89 88   50 14 49 81 06   01 82 77 45 12
67 80 43 79 33   12 83 11 41 16   25 58 19 68 70   77 02 54 00 52   53 43 37 15 26
27 62 50 96 72   79 44 61 40 15   14 53 40 65 39   27 31 58 50 28   11 39 03 34 25
33 78 80 87 15   38 30 06 38 21   14 47 47 07 26   54 96 87 53 32   40 36 40 96 76
13 13 92 66 99   47 24 49 57 74   32 25 43 62 17   10 97 11 69 84   99 63 22 32 98
```

* Appendix I is reprinted with permission from Random Numbers III of Table XXXIII of R. A. Fisher and F. Yates, *Statistical Tables for Biological, Agricultural and Medical Research* (Edinburgh: Oliver & Boyd, Ltd.).

APPENDIX J

Fortran Computer Programs for Basic Statistical Operations

Program FSCHR

This program will compute the following:

1. Values of the binomial distribution
2. Values of the Poisson distribution
3. Sample mean and unbiased variance estimate for a set of numbers.

The program will do only one of these problems at a time, but cases may be stacked so that any number of any of the above problems may be done in one computer run. The following formulas are given below to define the functions referred to above.

1. Binomial:

$$f(x) = \frac{n!}{x!(n-x)!} \, p^x(1-p)^{n-x}; \qquad x = 0, 1, \ldots, n$$

2. Poisson:

$$f(x) = \frac{\lambda^x e^{-\lambda}}{x!}; \qquad x = 0, 1, \ldots$$

3. Sample mean:

$$\bar{x} = \frac{1}{n} \sum_{i=1}^{n} x_i$$

Unbiased variance estimate:

$$\hat{s}^2 = \frac{1}{n-1} \sum_{i=1}^{n} (x_i - \bar{x})^2$$

Input Description

Card 1 Comment card. This card may contain any information. It will be printed as the first line of output (usually used as identification).

Card 2 The integer $M = 1$, 2, or 3 any place in this card. This integer will have the following meaning.

> $M = 1$ compute binomial distribution
> $M = 2$ compute Poisson distribution
> $M = 3$ compute sample mean and variance estimate

Card 3 ($M = 1$)—The integers n, x_1, x_2, x_3, and the decimal number p described below. These variables may be located anywhere on the card but must be separated by commas.

Variable	Definition
n	n in binomial distribution
x_1	initial value of x in binomial distribution
x_2	final value of x in binomial distribution
x_3	incremental value of x in binomial distribution
p	p in binomial distribution

Card 3 ($M = 2$)—The integers x_1, x_2, x_3 and the decimal number p. These numbers are the same as the corresponding numbers in the binomial distribution except they apply to the Poisson distribution.

Card 3 ($M = 3$)—The integer n and the real numbers $x_1, x_2, \ldots, x_n$. (See sample mean and variance). These numbers again may be located anywhere on the card but must be separated by commas.

Fortran Program for FSCHR

```
      DIMENSION COM(14), X(500)
      REAL MOMM
    7 CONTINUE
      READ (5,500)COM
  500 FORMAT(13A6,A2)
      WRITE(6,600) COM
  600 FORMAT(1H1,20X,13A6,A2)
      READ (5,499) NOP
  499 FORMAT()
      WRITE(6,599) NOP
  599 FORMAT(1H0,I5)
      GO TO (1,2,3),NOP

      BINOMIAL DISTRIBUTION.
    1 CONTINUE
      READ (5,499)NN,K1,K2,K3,P
      WRITE(6,601)NN,K1,K2,K3,P
  601 FORMAT(1H0,4I5,E16.8)
      L1=K1+1
      L2=K2+1
      WRITE(6,602)
  602 FORMAT(1H0,8X,1HX,13X,4HF(X))
      DO 10 I=L1,L2,K3
      J=I-1
      XX=BIN(NN,J,P,NER)
      IF(NER.EQ.2) GO TO 50
      WRITE(6,603) J,XX
  603 FORMAT(1H0,I10,5X,E16.8)
   10 CONTINUE
      GO TO 7

C     POISSON DISTRIBUTION.
    2 CONTINUE
      READ (5,499) K1,K2,K3,XL
      WRITE(6,801)K1,K2,K3,XL
  801 FORMAT(1H0,4X,3I5,E16.8)
      L1=K1+1
      L2=K2+1
      WRITE(6,602)
      DO 20 I=L1,L2,K3
      J=I-1
      XX=POIS(J,XL)
   20 WRITE(6,603) J,XX
      GO TO 7

C     MEAN AND STANDARD DEVIATION.
    3 CONTINUE
      READ (5,499) N,(X(I),I=1,N)
      WRITE(6,502) N, (X(I),I=1,N)
  502 FORMAT(1H0,I5/(5E16.8))
      XBAR=MOMM(X,0.,N,1)
      S2=MOMM(X,XBAR,N,2)
      A=FLOAT(N)/FLOAT(N-1)*S2
      WRITE (6,605)XBAR,A
  605 FORMAT(1H0,15X,4HMEAN,17X,8HVARIANCE      /8X,E16.8,7X,E16.8)
      GO TO 7
   50 CONTINUE
      WRITE(6,700)
  700 FORMAT(31H0ERROR IN INPUT--GET NEXT CASE.)
      GO TO 7
      STOP
      END
```

Fortran Program for FSCHR (cont'd.)

```
      REAL FUNCTION BIN(NN,NX,P,NER)
      NER=1

C     COMPUTE FACTORIALS.
      IF(NX.EQ.0.OR.NX.EQ.NN)GO TO 4
      IF(NX.EQ.1.OR.NX.EQ.NN-1) GO TO 5
      IF(NN.LT.NX.OR.P.GT.1.) GO TO 6
      F=1.
      XF=1.
      XMF=1.
      DO 1 I=2,NX
      XF=XF*FLOAT(I)
    1 F=F*FLOAT(I)
      K=NX+1
      DO 2 I=K,NN
    2 F=F*FLOAT(I)
      K=NN-NX
      DO 3 I=2,K
    3 XMF=XMF*FLOAT(I)

C     COMPUTE BINOMIAL COEFFICIENTS.
      C=F/(XF*XMF)

   10 CONTINUE
C     COMPUTE BIN.
      K=NN-NX
      BIN=C*P**NX*(1.-P)**K
      RETURN
    6 NER=2
      RETURN
    4 C=1.
      GO TO 10
    5 C=FLOAT(NN)
      GO TO 10
      END



      REAL FUNCTION POIS(NX,XL)

C     COMPUTE X FACTORIAL.
      FX=1.
      IF(NX.EQ.0) GO TO 3
      DO 1 I=1,NX
    1 FX=FX*FLOAT(I)

C     COMPUTE POIS.
    3 CONTINUE
      POIS=XL**NX*EXP(-XL)/FX
      RETURN
      END
```

187

Fortran Program for FSCHR (cont'd.)

```
      REAL FUNCTION MOMM(X,XM,N,M)
C     THIS ROUTINE COMPUTES THE M TH MOMENT ABOUT XM OF THE N NOS. IN X.
      DIMENSION X(N)
      Y=0.
      DO 10 I=1,N
   10 Y=Y+(X(I)-XM)**M
      MOMM=Y/FLOAT(N)
      RETURN
      END
```

```
                 SAMPLE OF INPUT
COMMENT CARD--MAY CONTAIN ANY INFORMATION    (BINOMIAL)
   1
 20,0,20,2,   .1
COMMENT CARD--MAY CONTAIN ANY INFORMATION    (POISSON)
   2
 0,30,3,2.0
COMMENT CARD--MAY CONTAIN ANY INFORMATION    (MEAN AND. ST. DEV.)
   3
      9
 1., 2., 3., 4., 5., 6.
   7., 8., 9.
```

Program CRVREG (Curvilinear Regression Analysis)

This program will solve the matrix equation $C \times B = D$ for the vector B where

$$C = p \times p \text{ matrix}$$
$$B = p \times 1 \text{ vector}$$
$$D = p \times 1 \text{ vector}$$

The C matrix and D vector are defined as follows:

$$C_{ij} = \sum_{k=1}^{n} (x_k^i - \overline{x^i})(x_k^j - \overline{x^j}); \qquad (i, j = 1, \ldots p)$$

$$D_{i1} = \sum_{k=1}^{n} (y_k - y)(x_k^i - \overline{x^i}); \qquad (i = 1, \ldots p)$$

where

$$\overline{x^i} = \frac{1}{n} \sum_{k=1}^{n} x_k^i$$

The program will print out these matrices as part of the output.

The solution vector is of the form $(B_{i1}, i = 1, \ldots, p)$; however, the program will also compute the element B_0 where

188

$$B_0 = y - \sum_{i=1}^{p} B_{i1}\overline{x^i}$$

and print this out as part of the solution vector.

In addition, the program will print an analysis of variance table as follows:

ANALYSIS OF VARIANCE TABLE

	Sum of Squares	D.F.	Mean Square
Due to Regression	$CY1$	P	$C1$
About Regression	$CY2$	$n - P - 1$	$C2$
Total	CYY	$n - 1$	CY

Where:

$$CYY = \sum_{i=1}^{n} (y_i - y)^2 \qquad CY = CYY/(n-1)$$

$$CY1 = \sum_{i=1}^{p} B_{i1}D_{i1} \qquad C1 = CY1/p$$

$$CY2 = CYY - CY1 \qquad C2 = CY2/(n-p-1)$$

Input Description

Card 1 Comment card.

Card 2 The integers p, n (in that order) described above. These integers may be located anywhere on the card and must be separated by a comma.

Card 3a, 3b, ... The numbers x_i, $i = 1, \ldots, n$. These numbers may be located anywhere on the card but must be separated by commas.

Card 4a, 4b, ... The numbers y_i, $i = 1, \ldots, n$. These numbers may be located anywhere on the card but must be separated by commas as above.

Fortran Program for CRVREG

```
      DIMENSION X(50),Y(50),XM(50),C(50,50),D(50,50),E(50),B(50,50)
      DIMENSION COM(14)
      DIMENSION DD(50,50)
      EQUIVALENCE(C,B)
      INTEGER P
      INTEGER E
      REAL MOM

C     NEXT CASE.
    1 CONTINUE
      READ (5,499) COM
  499 FORMAT(13A6,A2)
      WRITE(6,599) COM
  599 FORMAT(1H1,20X,13A6,A2)

C     READ AND WRITE INPUT USING FREE FIELD FORMAT.
C     DATA MUST BE SEPARATED BY COMMAS.
      READ (5,501)P,N
  501 FORMAT()
      READ (5,501) (X(I),I=1,N)
      READ(5,501)(Y(I),I=1,N)
      WRITE(6,552)
  552 FORMAT(1H0,20X,5HINPUT)
      WRITE(6,550)P,N
  550 FORMAT(1H0,2I5)
      WRITE(6,551) (X(I),I=1,N)
      WRITE(6,551) (Y(I),I=1,N)
  551 FORMAT(1H0,(5E16.8))

C     COMPUTE MOMENTS.
      DO 10 I=1,P
   10 XM(I)=MOM(X,N,I)
      YM=MOM(Y,N,1)


C     COMPUTE COEFFICIENTS.
      DO 20 J=1,P
      D(J,1)=REG(N,1,J,Y,X,YM,XM(J))
      DO 20 K=J,P
      IF(J.GT.K) GO TO 20
      C(J,K)=REG(N,J,K,X,X,XM(J),XM(K))
      C(K,J)=C(J,K)
   20 CONTINUE

C     WRITE OUT COEFFICIENT MATRIX.
      WRITE(6,605)
      WRITE(6,604)
  604 FORMAT(1H0,20X,18HCOEFFICIENT MATRIX)
      DO 100 I=1,P
  100 WRITE(6,601) (C(I,J),J=1,P)
      WRITE(6,605)
  605 FORMAT(1H0,/)
      WRITE(6,601) (D(J,1),J=1,P)
      DO 70 I=1,P
   70 DD(I,1)=D(I,1)
      WRITE(6,605)

C     SOLVE THE MATRIX EQUATION C B = D FOR B USING SIMEQ.
      M=1
      CALL SIMEQ(50,P,1,C,D,0.,E,M)
```

```
C       WRITE RESULTS.
        GO TO (30,40,50),M
   30 CONTINUE
        WRITE (6,600)
  600 FORMAT(1H0,20X,15HSOLUTION VECTOR)
        W=0.
        DO 60 I=1,P
   60 W=W+B(I,1)*XM(I)
        BZ=YM-W
        WRITE(6,601)BZ,(B(I,1),I=1,P)
  601 FORMAT(1H0,5E20.8)

C       WRITE ANOVA TABLE.
        WRITE(6,605)
        CALL ANOVA(Y,YM,N,P,B,DD)
        GO TO 1

   40 CONTINUE
        WRITE(6,602)
  602 FORMAT(36HOUNDERFLOW OR OVERFLOW HAS OCCURRED.)
        GO TO 30
   50 CONTINUE
        WRITE(6,603)
  603 FORMAT(44HOMATRIX IS SINGULAR--NO SOLUTION POSSIBLE.
       114HGET NEXT CASE.)
        WRITE(6,604)
        DO 101 I=1,P
  101 WRITE(6,601)  (C(I,J),J=1,P)
        WRITE(6,605)
        WRITE(6,601)  (D(J,1),J=1,P)
        GO TO 1
        END


        REAL FUNCTION MOM (X,N,M)

C       THIS ROUTINE CALCULATES THE M'TH MOMENT ABOUT ZERO  OF THE N NUMBERS
C       STORED IN X.

        DIMENSION X(N)
        XM=0.
        IF(M.EQ.1) GO TO 11
        DO 10 I=1,N
   10 XM=XM+X(I)**M
        GO TO 13
   11 DO 12 I=1,N
   12 XM=XM+X(I)
   13 MOM=XM/FLOAT(N)
        RETURN
        END


        REAL FUNCTION REG(P,J,K,X,Y,XM,YM)
C       THIS ROUTINE COMPUTES THE GENERAL COEFFICIENT-

C               P
C             ****
C              *      J           K
C       REG =  * ( X(I) -XM )*( Y(I) -YM )
C              *
C             ****
C              I=1

        INTEGER P
        DIMENSION X(50),Y(50)
        SUM=0.
        DO 10 I=1,P
   10 SUM = SUM+(X(I)**J-XM)*(Y(I)**K-YM)
        REG=SUM
        RETURN
        END
```

191

```
      REAL FUNCTION MOMM(X,XM,N,M)

C     THIS ROUTINE COMPUTES THE M TH MOMENT ABOUT XM OF THE N NOS. IN X.

      DIMENSION X(N)
      Y=0.
      DO 10 I=1,N
   10 Y=Y+(X(I)-XM)**M
      MOMM=Y/FLOAT(N)
      RETURN
      END


      SUBROUTINE ANOVA(Y,YM,N,P,B,D)
      INTEGER P
      REAL MOMM
      DIMENSION Y(N)
      DIMENSION B(P,1),D(P,1)
      WRITE(6,102)
  102 FORMAT(1H0,20X,27HANALYSIS OF VARIANCE TABLE.)
      CYY=MOMM(Y,YM,N,2)
      CYY=CYY*FLOAT(N)
      CY1=0.
      DO 10 I=1,P
   10 CY1=CY1+B(I,1)*D(I,1)
      CY2=CYY-CY1
      L=N-1
      K=L-P
      C1=CY1/FLOAT(P)
      C2=CY2/FLOAT(K)
      CY=CYY/FLOAT(L)
      WRITE(6,100)
  100 FORMAT(1H0,27X,14HSUM OF SQUARES,8X,4HD.F.,15X,11HMEAN SQUARE)
      WRITE(6,101) CY1,P,C1,CY2,K,C2,CYY,L,CY
  101 FORMAT(1H0,17HDUE TO REGRESSION,10X,E16.8,5X,I5,10X,E16.8//1X,
     116HABOUT REGRESSION,11X,E16.8,5X,I5,10X,E16.8//1X,
     115HTOTAL,22X,E16.8,5X,I5,10X,E16.8)
      RETURN
      END


      SUBROUTINE SIMEQ(N,LN,LM,A,B,D,E,M)
      INTEGER E
      EQUIVALENCE (SAVE,ISAVE)
      DIMENSION E(LN),A(N,N),B(N,LM)
      IF (M.EQ.0)    GO TO 2
      DO 1 I=1,LN
    1 E(I)=I
    2 LNM1=LN-1
      CALL OVERFL   (IBIG)
      DO 139 K=1,LNM1
      SAVE=-1.0
      K1=K+1
      DO 4 J=K,LN
      DO 4 I=K,LN
      IF (SAVE - ABS(A(I,J)))  3,4,4
    3 SAVE=ABS(A(I,J))
      IBIG=I
      JBIG=J
    4 CONTINUE
      IF (K.EQ.IBIG)   GO TO 61
      D=-D
      DO 6 J=K,LN
      SAVE=A(K,J)
      A(K,J)=A(IBIG,J)
    6 A(IBIG,J)=SAVE
      IF (M.EQ.0)    GO TO 61
      DO 7 J=1,LM
      SAVE=B(K,J)
      B(K,J)=B(IBIG,J)
```

```
7        B(IBIG,J)=SAVE
61       IF (K-JBIG) 8,89,8
8        D=-D
         DO 9 I=1,LN
         SAVE=A(I,K)
         A(I,K)=A(I,JBIG)
9        A(I,JBIG)=SAVE
         IF (M.EQ.0)    GO TO 89
         ISAVE=E(K)
         E(K)=E(JBIG)
         E(JBIG)=ISAVE
89       IF (A(K,K))    600,10,600
600      D=D*A(K,K)
         DO 139 I=K1,LN
         SAVE=A(I,K)/A(K,K)
         DO 15 J=K1,LN
15       A(I,J)=A(I,J)-SAVE*A(K,J)
         CALL OVERFL(IBIG)
         IF (IBIG-1)    710,12,710
710      IF (M.EQ.0)    GO TO 139
         DO 138 J=1,LM
138      B(I,J)=B(I,J)-SAVE*B(K,J)
         CALL OVERFL(IBIG)
         IF (IBIG-1)    139,12,139
139      CONTINUE
         IF (A(LN,LN))    601,10,601
601      IF(LN.NE.1) D=D*A(LN,LN)
         CALL OVERFL(IBIG)
         IF (IBIG-1)    150,12,150
150      IF (M) 118,250,118
118      DO 20 J=1,LM
         B(LN,J)=B(LN,J)/A(LN,LN)
         CALL OVERFL(IBIG)
         IF (IBIG-1)    18,12,18
18       DO 20 JBIG=1,LNM1
         I=LN-JBIG
         SAVE=0.
         IP1=I+1
         DO 19 K=IP1,LN
19       SAVE=SAVE+A(I,K)*B(K,J)
         B(I,J)=(B(I,J)-SAVE)/A(I,I)
         CALL OVERFL(IBIG)
         IF (IBIG-1)    20,12,20
20       CONTINUE
         DO 21 K=1,LN
         I=E(K)
         DO 21 J=1,LM
21       A(I,J)=B(K,J)
250      M=1
         RETURN
12       M=2
         RETURN
10       M=3
         RETURN
         END
```

```
                 SAMPLE OF INPUT
   USERS COMMENT--MAY CONTAIN ANY INFORMATION.
     2 ,    11
   -5.,    -4.,   -3.,   -2.,   -1.,   0.,   1.,   2.,   3.,   4.,   5.
   23.2,   31.4,   39.6,   50.2,   62.9,   76.0,   92.0,  105.7,  122.8,
  131.7,  151.1
```

Program MLREG (Multiple Linear Regression Analysis)

This program is very similar to CRVREG. The *differences* are indicated below:

$$C_{ij} = \sum_{k=1}^{n} (x_{ki} - \bar{x}_i)(x_{kj} - \bar{x}_j); \qquad (i, j = 1, \ldots, p)$$

$$D_{i1} = \sum_{k=1}^{n} (y_k - \bar{y})(x_{ki} - \bar{x}_i)$$

where

$$\bar{x}_i = \frac{1}{n} \sum_{k=1}^{n} x_{ki} \qquad\qquad (i = 1, \ldots, p)$$

$$B_0 = \bar{y} - \sum_{i=1}^{p} B_{i1}\bar{x}_i$$

The input will be the same except for card 3a, 3b. Card 3a, 3b, ... The numbers $x_{ij}, i = 1, \ldots, n, j = 1, \ldots, p$, i.e., the numbers must be read in as follows:

$$x_{11}, x_{21}, \ldots x_{n1}, x_{12}, x_{21}, \ldots \text{etc.}$$

Fortran Program for MLREG

```
      DIMENSION X(50,50),Y(50),XM(50),C(50,50),D(50,50),E(50),B(50,50)
      DIMENSION COM(14)
      DIMENSION DD(50,50)
      EQUIVALENCE(C,B)
      INTEGER P
      INTEGER E
      REAL MOM

C     NEXT CASE.
    1 CONTINUE
      READ (5,499) COM
  499 FORMAT(13A6,A2)
      WRITE(6,599) COM
  599 FORMAT(1H1,20X,13A6,A2)

C     READ AND WRITE INPUT USING FREE FIELD FORMAT.
C     DATA MUST BE SEPARATED BY COMMAS.
      READ (5,501)P,N
  501 FORMAT()
      READ (5,501) ((X(I,J),I=1,N),J=1,P)
      READ(5,501)(Y(I),I=1,N)
      WRITE(6,552)
  552 FORMAT(1H0,20X,5HINPUT)
      WRITE(6,550)P,N
  550 FORMAT(1H0,2I5)
      WRITE(6,551) ((X(I,J),I=1,N),J=1,P)
      WRITE(6,551) (Y(I),I=1,N)
  551 FORMAT(1H0,(5E16.8))

C     COMPUTE MOMENTS.
      DO 10 I=1,P
   10 XM(I)=MOM(X(1,I),N,1)
      YM=MOM(Y,N,1)

C     COMPUTE COEFFICIENTS.
      DO 20 J=1,P
      D(J,1)=REG(N,1,1,Y,X(1,J),YM,XM(J))
      DO 20 K=J,P
      IF(J.GT.K) GO TO 20
      C(J,K)=REG(N,1,1,X(1,J),X(1,K),XM(J),XM(K))
      C(K,J)=C(J,K)
   20 CONTINUE

C     WRITE OUT COEFFICIENT MATRIX.
      WRITE(6,605)
      WRITE(6,604)
  604 FORMAT(1H0,20X,18HCOEFFICIENT MATRIX)
      DO 100 I=1,P
  100 WRITE(6,601) (C(I,J),J=1,P)
      WRITE(6,605)
  605 FORMAT(1H0,/)
      WRITE(6,601) (D(J,1),J=1,P)
      DO 70 I=1,P
   70 DD(I,1)=D(I,1)
      WRITE(6,605)
```

Fortran Program for MLREG (cont'd.)

```
C       SOLVE THE MATRIX EQUATION C B = D FOR B USING SIMEQ.
        M=1

        CALL SIMEQ(50,P,1,C,D,0.,E,M)

C       WRITE RESULTS.
        GO TO (30,40,50),M
    30 CONTINUE
        WRITE (6,600)
   600 FORMAT(1H0,20X,15HSOLUTION VECTOR)
        W=0.
        DO 60 I=1,P
    60 W=W+B(I,1)*XM(I)
        BZ=YM-W
        WRITE(6,601)BZ,(B(I,1),I=1,P)
   601 FORMAT(1H0,5E20.8)

C       WRITE ANOVA TABLE.
        WRITE(6,605)
        CALL ANOVA(Y,YM,N,P,B,DD)
        GO TO 1

    40 CONTINUE
        WRITE(6,602)
   602 FORMAT(36HOUNDERFLOW OR OVERFLOW HAS OCCURRED.)
        GO TO 30
    50 CONTINUE
        WRITE(6,603)
   603 FORMAT(44HOMATRIX IS SINGULAR--NO SOLUTION POSSIBLE.
       114HGET NEXT CASE.)
        WRITE(6,604)
        DO 101 I=1,P
   101 WRITE(6,601) (C(I,J),J=1,P)
        WRITE(6,605)
        WRITE(6,601) (D(J,1),J=1,P)
        GO TO 1
        END


        REAL FUNCTION MOM (X,N,M)

C       THIS ROUTINE CALCULATES THE M'TH MOMENT ABOUT ZERO  OF THE N NUMBER
C       STORED IN X.

        DIMENSION X(N)
        XM=0.
        IF(M.EQ.1) GO TO 11
        DO 10 I=1,N
    10 XM=XM+X(I)**M
        GO TO 13
    11 DO 12 I=1,N
    12 XM=XM+X(I)
    13 MOM=XM/FLOAT(N)
        RETURN
        END
```

Fortran Program for MLREG (cont'd.)

```
      REAL FUNCTION REG(P,J,K,X,Y,XM,YM)
C     THIS ROUTINE COMPUTES THE GENERAL COEFFICIENT-
C
C               P
C              ****
C               *        J           K
C     REG =     *  ( X(I) -XM )*( Y(I) -YM )
C               *
C              ****
C               I=1
C
      INTEGER P
      DIMENSION X(50),Y(50)
      SUM=0.
      DO 10 I=1,P
   10 SUM = SUM+(X(I)**J-XM)*(Y(I)**K-YM)
      REG=SUM
      RETURN
      END



      REAL FUNCTION MOMM(X,XM,N,M)
C     THIS ROUTINE COMPUTES THE M TH MOMENT ABOUT XM OF THE N NOS. IN X.

      DIMENSION X(N)
      Y=0.
      DO 10 I=1,N
   10 Y=Y+(X(I)-XM)**M
      MOMM=Y/FLOAT(N)
      RETURN
      END


      SUBROUTINE ANOVA(Y,YM,N,P,B,D)
      INTEGER P
      REAL MOMM
      DIMENSION Y(N)
      DIMENSION B(P,1),D(P,1)
      WRITE(6,102)
  102 FORMAT(1H0,20X,27HANALYSIS OF VARIANCE TABLE.)
      CYY=MOMM(Y,YM,N,2)
      CYY=CYY*FLOAT(N)
      CY1=0.
      DO 10 I=1,P
   10 CY1=CY1+B(I,1)*D(I,1)
      CY2=CYY-CY1
      L=N-1
      K=L-P
      C1=CY1/FLOAT(P)
      C2=CY2/FLOAT(K)
      CY=CYY/FLOAT(L)
      WRITE(6,100)
  100 FORMAT(1H0,27X,14HSUM OF SQUARES,8X,4HD.F.,15X,11HMEAN SQUARE)
      WRITE(6,101) CY1,P,C1,CY2,K,C2,CYY,L,CY
```

Fortran Program for MLREG (cont'd.)

```
 101    FORMAT(1H0,17HDUE TO REGRESSION,10X,E16.8,5X,I5,10X,E16.8//1X,
       116HABOUT REGRESSION,11X,E16.8,5X,I5,10X,E16.8//1X,
       15HTOTAL,22X,E16.8,5X,I5,10X,E16.8)
        RETURN
        END


        SUBROUTINE SIMEQ(N,LN,LM,A,B,D,E,M)
        INTEGER E
        EQUIVALENCE (SAVE,ISAVE)
        DIMENSION E(LN),A(N,N),B( N,LM)
        IF (M.EQ.0)     GO TO 2
        DO 1 I=1,LN
 1      E(I)=I
 2      LNM1=LN-1
        CALL OVERFL  (IBIG)
        DO 139 K=1,LNM1
        SAVE=-1.0
        K1=K+1
        DO 4 J=K,LN
        DO 4 I=K,LN
        IF (SAVE - ABS(A(I,J)))  3,4,4
 3      SAVE=ABS(A(I,J))
        IBIG=I
        JBIG=J
 4      CONTINUE
        IF (K.EQ.IBIG)  GO TO 61
        D=-D
        DO 6 J=K,LN
        SAVE=A(K,J)
        A(K,J)=A(IBIG,J)
 6      A(IBIG,J)=SAVE
        IF (M.EQ.0)    GO TO 61
        DO 7 J=1,LM
        SAVE=B(K,J)
        B(K,J)=B(IBIG,J)
 7      B(IBIG,J)=SAVE
 61     IF (K-JBIG) 8,89,8
 8      D=-D
        DO 9 I=1,LN
        SAVE=A(I,K)
        A(I,K)=A(I,JBIG)
 9      A(I,JBIG)=SAVE
        IF (M.EQ.0)    GO TO 89
        ISAVE=E(K)
        E(K)=E(JBIG)
        E(JBIG)=ISAVE
 89     IF (A(K,K))  600,10,600
 600    D=D*A(K,K)
        DO 139 I=K1,LN
        SAVE=A(I,K)/A(K,K)
        DO 15 J=K1,LN
 15     A(I,J)=A(I,J)-SAVE*A(K,J)
        CALL OVERFL(IBIG)
        IF (IBIG-1)   710,12,710
 710    IF (M.EQ.0)   GO TO 139
```

Fortran Program for MLREG (cont'd.)

```
        DO 138 J=1,LM
138     B(I,J)=B(I,J)-SAVE*B(K,J)
        CALL OVERFL(IBIG)
        IF (IBIG-1)      139,12,139
139     CONTINUE
        IF (A(LN,LN))    601,10,601
601     IF(LN.NE.1) D=D*A(LN,LN)
        CALL OVERFL(IBIG)
        IF (IBIG-1)      150,12,150
150     IF (M) 118,250,118
118     DO 20 J=1,LM
        B(LN,J)=B(LN,J)/A(LN,LN)
        CALL OVERFL(IBIG)
        IF (IBIG-1)      18,12,18
18      DO 20 JBIG=1,LNM1
        I=LN-JBIG
        SAVE=0.
        IP1=I+1
        DO 19 K=IP1,LN
19      SAVE=SAVE+A(I,K)*B(K,J)
        B(I,J)=(B(I,J)-SAVE)/A(I,I)
        CALL OVERFL(IBIG)
        IF (IBIG-1)      20,12,20
20      CONTINUE
        DO 21 K=1,LN
        I=E(K)
        DO 21 J=1,LM
21      A(I,J)=B(K,J)
250     M=1
        RETURN
12      M=2
        RETURN
10      M=3
        RETURN
        END
```

```
                 SAMPLE OF INPUT
USERS COMMENT--MAY CONTAIN ANY INFORMATION.
   2,12
57.0,59.0,49.0,62.0,51.0,50.0,55.0,48.0,52.0,42.0,  61.0,57.0,8.0,10.0,6.0,11.0
8.0,7.0,10.0,9.0,10.0,6.0,12.0,9.0
64.0,71.0,53.0,67.0,55.0,58.0,77.0,57.0,56.0,51.0,76.0,68.0
```

199

BIBLIOGRAPHY

1. Beer, Ferdinand P., E. Russell Johnston, Jr., *Mechanics for Engineers Statics and Dynamics*, Second Edition, McGraw-Hill Book Company, Inc., New York, 1962.
2. Bennett, Carl A., Norman L. Franklin, *Statistical Analysis in Chemistry and the Chemical Industry*, John Wiley and Sons, Inc., New York, 1954.
3. Beveridge, W. I. B., *The Art of Scientific Investigation*, W. W. Norton and Company, Inc., New York, 1957.
4. Bowker, Albert H., Gerald J. Lieberman, *Engineering Statistics*, Prentice-Hall, Inc., Englewood Cliffs, New Jersey, 1959.
5. Brownlee, K. A., *Industrial Experimentation*, Fourth American Edition, Chemical Publishing Company, Inc., New York, 1953.
6. Cochran, William G., Gertrude M. Cox, *Experimental Designs*, Second Edition, John Wiley and Sons, Inc., New York, 1957.
7. Cohen, Morris R., Ernest Nagel, *An Introduction to Logic and Scientific Method*, Harcourt, Brace and Company, New York, 1934.
8. Cramer, Harald, *The Elements of Probability Theory*, Sixth Printing, John Wiley and Sons, Inc., New York, 1961.
9. Davies, Owen L. (ed.), *Statistical Methods in Research and Production*, Hafner Publishing Company, New York, 1961.
10. ———, (ed.), *The Design and Analysis of Industrial Experiments*, Hafner Publishing Company, New York, 1960.
11. Deming, W. Edwards, *Statistical Adjustment of Data*, John Wiley and Sons, Inc., New York, 1938.

12. Duncan, J. Acheson, *Quality Control and Industrial Statistics*, Richard D. Irwin, Inc., Homewood, Illinois, 1959.
13. Fisher, R. A., *The Design of Experiments*, Second Edition, Oliver and Boyd, Ltd., London, 1937.
14. ———, *Statistical Methods for Research Workers*, Fifth Edition, Oliver and Boyd, London, 1934.
15. Freedman, Paul, *The Principles of Scientific Research*, Pergamon Press, New York, 1960.
16. Geffner, Joseph, Archie G. Worthing, *Treatment of Experimental Data*, John Wiley and Sons, Inc., New York, 1943.
17. Hald, Anders, *Statistical Theory With Engineering Applications*, John Wiley and Sons, Inc., New York, 1955.
18. Hicks, Charles R., *Fundamental Concepts in the Design of Experiments*, Holt, Rinehart and Winston, Inc., New York, 1964.
19. Higdon, Archie, William B. Stiles, *Engineering Mechanics*, Second Edition, Prentice-Hall, Inc., Englewood Cliffs, New Jersey, 1948.
20. Hoel, Paul G., *Introduction to Mathematical Statistics*, Second Edition, Seventh Printing, John Wiley and Sons, Inc., New York, 1961.
21. Palmer, A. De Forest, *The Theory of Measurements*, McGraw-Hill Book Company, Inc. New York, 1912.
22. Spiegel, Murray R., *Theory and Problems of Statistics*, Schaum Publishing Company, New York, 1961.
23. Tippett, L. H. C., *Technological Applications of Statistics*, John Wiley and Sons, Inc., New York, 1950.
24. Wightman, William P. D., *The Growth of Scientific Ideas*, Yale University, New Haven, Conn., 1951.
25. Wilson, E. Bright, Jr., *An Introduction to Scientific Research*, McGraw-Hill Book Company, New York, 1952.

Index

About the regression sum of squares, 64, 91
Addition theorem, 14
α as area under the normal curve, 31
α as error of the first kind, 105
Alternate hypothesis, 105
Analysis, 3, 7, 100
  experiments with multiple independent variables, 83
  experiments with one independent variable, 55
  linear regression variance, 63
  multiple linear regression variance, 89
  variance, 63
    method, 79, 93
    regression method, 73
    table, 65
Analytical error, 121
ANOVA table, 65
Arithmetic mean, 45
Average deviation, 47

Belief, probability as measure of, 103
Best estimate, least squares, 73
Bias, 148
  nature of, 149
Binomial distribution, 16
  mean, 22
  second moment, 22
  standard deviation, 24
  variance, 24
Binomial expansion, 16
Binomial moments, 20
Binomial parameters, 20, 22

Cause and effect, 101
  nature of, 100
Central limit theorem, 52

Central tendency, measure of, 45
Chi square (χ^2) distribution, 33, 108
Coding, 60, 61
Coefficient of correlation, 114
  curvilinear, 120
  linear multiple, 119
Coefficient of determination, 114
Column effect, 73, 92
Column sum of squares, 77
Combination, 161, 163
Combinatorial analysis, 161
Common effect, 56, 92
Comparison of means, 140
  made after experimentation, 146
  made prior to experimentation, 144
Complete randomization, 151
Component of variance, 124, 128
Computer programs, 185
Conducting a search, 3
Confidence intervals as inference, 107
Confidence limits, 118
  for mean, μ, 136
  for regression estimate, 118
  for variances, 130
Contingency table, 168
Continuous frequency function, 28
  joint, 165
Continuous random variable, 28
Continuous mass, moments of, 28
Contrasts, independent, 42
Control variable, 144
Correlation, 114
  coefficient of, 114
  curvilinear, 119
    coefficient of, 120
  linear multiple, 119
    coefficient of, 120
  multiple, 119
Covariance, 43

Curvilinear correlation, 119
  coefficient, 120
Curvilinear regression, 67

Data distributions, 8
Deductive logic, 98
Deductive reasoning, 99
Degrees of freedom, 42
Dependent events, 10
Dependent variable, 56, 57, 101
Determination, coefficient of, 114
Deterministic view, 8
Difference between:
  several sample means, 144
  two sample means, 140
    when $\sigma^2_{y_1}$ and $\sigma^2_{y_2}$ are known, 140
    when $\sigma^2_{y_1}$ and $\sigma^2_{y_2}$ are unknown, 142
Discrete frequency function, 17
Discrete random variable, 17, 20
Distribution, 9
  chi square (χ^2), 33, 108
  Erlang, 33
  exponential, 33
  F, 33, 111
  geometric, 33
  of mean squares, 108
  r, 116
  of sample mean, 48
  t, 33, 111
  theoretical, 56, 72, 83, 92
  of variance, 129
Distribution function, 164
Dual-block randomization, 154
Due to regression sum of squares, 64, 89

Effect, 72
  column, 73, 92
  common mean, 92
  row, 92
Elements of sets, 9
Empirical methods, 36
Empirical moments, 38
Erlang distribution, 33
Error, 56
  analytical, 121
  of the first kind, 105
  random, 56, 72
  residual, 92
  sampling, 121
  of the second kind, 105
  standard, 49
    of the mean, 49
    of the regression estimate, 117
    Type I, 105
    Type II, 105

Estimate, 40
  best, 40
    of least squares, 73
    of mean, 45
  of intercept, 57
  regression, 118
    confidence limits for, 118
    standard error of, 117
  of slope, 57
  of standard deviation, 42
  unbiased, 40
  of variance, 40, 73
Events, 10
  dependent, 10
  independent, 10
  mutually exclusive, 10
Evidence, nature of, 101
Expected mean square, 123
Experiment, reproducible, 5
Experimental procedure, 4
Experimentation, preparation for, 4
Experiments:
  randomization in, 148
  with multiple independent variables, 83
    analysis of, 83
    interpretation of, 108
  with one independent variable, 55
    analysis of, 55
    interpretation of, 108
Exponential distribution, 33

F distribution, 33, 111
Facts, nature of, 99
First moment, 20, 22, 38
Formal logic, 98
Fortran computer program, 185
Frequency, relative, 103
  probability as, 103
Frequency, truth, 107
  probability as, 104
Frequency data, 167
  interpretation of, 167
Frequency function, 17
  continuous, 28
  discrete, 17
  joint continuous, 165
Function, 17
  continuous frequency, 28
  discrete frequency, 17
  distribution, 164
  joint continuous frequency, 165

Gamma function, 109
Gausian distribution, 28

Geometric, 33
  distribution, 33
  mean, 46
Gossett, W. S., 111
Graeco-Latin square experiment, 157

Harmonic mean, 46
Histogram, 18
Hypothesis, 4, 99
  alternate, 105
  nature of, 102
  null, 105

Independent, 10
  contrasts, 42
  events, 10
  variable, 56, 101
Indifference, principle of, 103
Inductive reasoning, 104
Inference, 100
  confidence intervals as, 107
  Neyman-Pearson theory of, 105
  probable, 102
  statistical, 104
Intercept, 57
  estimate of, 57, 84
  true, 57
    for curvilinear regression, 67
    for linear regression, 56
    for multiple linear regression, 84
Interpretation, 7, 100
  of frequency data, 167
  of means, 133
  of μ when σ is unknown, 138
  of probability, 102
  theory of, 98
  of variances, 108
Intervals:
  confidence, 118
    as inference, 107

Joint continuous frequency function, 165

Latin square experiment, 154
Least squares, 57
  best estimates, 73
  derivation of method of, 57
Levels:
  of significance, 105
  of variables not predetermined, 55, 83
  of variables predetermined, 55, 72, 92
Limits, confidence, 118
  for mean, 136
  for regression estimate, 118
  for variance, 130

Linear correlation, 114
  coefficient of, 114
    multiple, 119
Linear regression, 56
  multiple, 84
    estimated intercept for, 84
    estimated slope for, 84
    true intercept for, 84
    true slope for, 84
    variance, analysis of, 89
  true intercept of, 57
  true slope of, 57
  variance, analysis of, 63
Logic, 2
  deductive, 98
  formal, 98

Mathematical model, 56, 72, 92
Mean, 22
  arithmetic, 45
  of binomial distribution, 22
  geometric, 46
  harmonic, 46
  quadratic, 47
  standard error of, 49
Mean square, 64
  distribution of, 108
  expected, 123
Means, 132
  comparison of, 144
    after experimentation, 146
    prior to experimentation, 144
  difference between several sample, 144
  difference between two sample, 140
    when $\sigma_{y_1}^2$ and $\sigma_{y_2}^2$ are known, 140
    when $\sigma_{y_1}^2$ and $\sigma_{y_2}^2$ are unknown, 142
  interpretation of, 132
Measures of variation, 47
Median, 45
Method of least squares, 52
Mode, 45
Model, mathematical, 92
Moment generating function, 29, 49, 110
Moments, 20
  about the origin, 38
  binomial, 20
  empirical, 38
  first, 20, 22
  of inertia, 29
  of normal distribution, 28
  of point mass, 20, 21
  statical, 28
  statistical, 29
μ, the mean, 22
  confidence limits for, 136
  interpretation of, 138

Multidual-block randomization, 157
Multiple linear:
  correlation, 119
    coefficient of, 119
  regression, 84
    estimated intercept for, 84
    estimated slope for, 84
    true intercept for, 84
    true slope for, 84
    variance analysis, 89
Mutually exclusive events, 10

Nature of:
  bias, 149
  cause and effect, 100
  evidence, 101
  facts, 99
  hypotheses, 102
  proof, 100
Neyman-Pearson theory, 105
Normal distribution, 27, 28
  moments of, 28
Null hypothesis, 105
Null sets, 9

One-tail test, 134
Operating characteristic curve, 107, 135
Origin, moments about, 38

Parabolic regression, 70
Permutation, 16, 161
Poisson distribution, 24
Power of a test, 107
Preparation for experimentation, 4
Principle of:
  indifference, 103
  insufficient reason, 103
Probabilistic view, 8
Probability, 101
  interpretation of, 102
  introduction to, 9
  as measure of belief, 103
  as relative frequency, 103
  sample space, 11
  simple, 11
  as truth frequency, 104
Probable inference, 102
Procedure, experimental, 4
Product theorem, 14
Proof, nature of, 100

Quadratic mean, 47
Quartile deviation, 48

r, distribution of, 116

Random:
  error, 56, 72
  sample, 56, 83
  sampling, 6, 37
  variable
    continuous, 28
    discrete, 17, 20
    standardized normal, 31
Randomization, 4
  complete, 151
  dual block, 154
  in experiments, 148
  multidual block, 157
  single block, 154
Randomized block experiment, 154
Range, 47
Real effect, 56
Reason, principle of insufficient, 103
Reasoning, 99
  deductive, 99
  inductive, 104
Regression, 56
  curvilinear, 67
  estimate, 57, 84
    confidence limits for, 118
    standard error of, 117
  linear, 56
    analysis of variance for, 63
    estimated intercept for, 57
    estimated slope for, 57
    true intercept of, 56
    true slope of, 56
  method of variance analysis, 73
  multiple linear, 84
    estimated intercept for, 84
    estimated slope for, 84
    true intercept for, 84
    true slope for, 84
  parabolic, 70
  sum of squares, 77, 89
    about the, 64, 91
    due to, 64, 89
  variance, 63
    linear, 63
    multiple linear, 89
Relative frequency, probability as, 103
Reproducible experiments, 5
Residual error, 92
Responses, 37
Root mean square, 47
Row effect, 92

Sample, 36
  mean, 48
  points, 13
  size of, 133, 135

space probability, 11
spaces, 9
standard deviation, 38
variance, 38
Sampling, 36
    error, 121
    random, 6, 37
Scientific method, 1
Search, conducting a, 3
Second moment, 22
    of binomial distribution, 22
    empirical, 38
    of normal distribution, 31
Sets, 9
    null, 9
    elements of, 9
    intersection of, 9
Significance, level of, 105
Simple probability, 11
Simplification, 3
Single block randomization, 154
Size of sample, 133, 135
Slope, 57
    estimate of, 57
        for multiple linear regression, 84
    true, 57
        for linear regression, 56
        for multiple linear regression, 84
Standard error, 49
    of the mean, 49
    of the regression estimate, 117
Standard deviation, 24
    of binomial distribution, 24
    of sample, 38
Standardized normal random variable, 31
Statement of the problem, 3
Statical moment, 28
Statistical,
    inference, 104
    moments, 29
    theory, 7
Student's t distribution, 111
Sum of squares, 63
    about the regression, 64, 91

column, 77
    due to regression, 64, 89
    regression, 77, 89
Summed products, 69
Synthesis, 3

t distribution, 33, 111
Test, power of a, 107
Theoretical distribution, 56, 72, 83, 92
Theory of interpretation, 98
Theory, statistical, 7
True intercept, 57
    for linear regression, 57
    for multiple linear regression, 84
True slope, 57
    for linear regression, 57
    for multiple linear regression, 84
Truth-frequency, 107
    theory, 104
Two-tail test, 139, 169

Unbiased estimate of σ^2, 40

Variable, 4
    control, 144
    dependent, 56, 57, 83, 101
    independent, 55, 83, 101
    predetermined levels of, 92
Variance, 24
    analysis of, 63
        linear regression, 63
        method, 93
        multiple linear regression, 89
        regression method of, 73
    of binomial distribution, 24
    component of, 124, 128
    confidence limits for, 130
    distribution of, 129
    estimate of, 40, 73
    interpretation of, 108
    sample, 38
    unbiased estimate of, 40
Variation, measure of, 47